How to Teach Maths

CW00558118

How to Teach Maths challenges everything you thought you knew about how maths is taught in classrooms. Award-winning author Steve Chinn casts a critical eye over many of the long-established methods and beliefs of maths teaching. Drawing from decades of classroom experience and research, he shows how mathematics teaching across the whole ability range can be radically improved by learning from the successful methods and principles used for the bottom quartile of achievers: the outliers. Chinn guides readers through re-adjusting the presentation of maths to learners, considering learners' needs first, and explains the importance of securing early learning to create a conceptual foundation for later success.

This highly accessible book uses clear diagrams and examples to support maths teachers through many critical issues, including the following:

* The context of maths education today
* Topics that cause students the most difficulty
* Effective communication in the mathematics classroom
* Addressing maths anxiety

The perfect resource for maths teachers at all levels, this book is especially useful for those wanting to teach the foundations of mathematics in a developmental way to learners of all ages and abilities. It has the potential to change the way maths is taught forever.

Steve Chinn is a Visiting Professor at the University of Derby. He is the author of *The Trouble with Maths* and *More Trouble with Maths* and the editor of *The Routledge International Handbook of Dyscalculia and Mathematical Learning Difficulties.* He has lectured and provided teacher training in over 30 countries. He founded, and ran for two decades, an award-winning school for learners with specific learning difficulties.

First edition published 2021
by Routledge
2 Park Square, Milton Park, Abingdon, Oxon, OX14 4RN

and by Routledge
52 Vanderbilt Avenue, New York, NY 10017

Routledge is an imprint of the Taylor & Francis Group, an informa business

© 2021 Steve Chinn

British Library Cataloguing-in-Publication Data
A catalogue record for this book is available from the British Library

Library of Congress Cataloging-in-Publication Data
A catalog record has been requested for this book

ISBN: 978-0-367-86270-1 (hbk)
ISBN: 978-0-367-86271-8 (pbk)
ISBN: 978-1-003-01807-0 (ebk)

Typeset in Galliard
by SPi Global, India

Contents

Introduction

Let me try to establish my credentials, my sources of inspiration and my objectives for writing this book.

Over the past 27 years, I have written books on maths and dyslexia, maths learning difficulties and dyscalculia. The main ones are now in third and fourth editions. I have lectured, trained teachers and provided consultation on these topics in some 30 countries around the world. I have been head of three specialist schools for students with specific learning difficulties; one of these schools I founded. That school received two major awards, the Independent Schools Association's 'Award for Excellence' and 'Beacon School' status from the UK Government, which funded the provision of training on maths learning difficulties for other schools and for our pioneering work on assistive technology.

I have carried out extensive, school-based research into many facets of maths learning difficulties and dyscalculia.

My educational background and degrees are in chemistry and applied physics. I taught in mainstream schools for 14 years, including five years as the head of the maths and science faculty at a comprehensive school before moving to special education.

Thus, I have wide-ranging experience in mainstream and specialist schools, coupled with an international perspective that has provided me with an understanding of the similarities and the differences in the approaches and pedagogies used in a range of settings.

The outcome of this experience is this book. I know that much of what I have learned from working with the 'outliers' and comparing that with my time in mainstream is relevant across the spectrum of learners. I hope you, too, can be convinced of this or at least find some useful ideas and new perspectives.

The book has practical suggestions for use in the classroom, some thoughts on pedagogy, a few sceptical comments and some rationalisation and research background for all of those.

The title is an adaptation of a wise philosophy from Margaret Rawson, an inspirational educator from the US. It is a succinct principle for education:

Teach the subject as it is to the child as he is.

So, to teach the child (or adult), we need to understand what it is we are teaching and match that to a comprehensive knowledge of our learners. We need these understandings and knowledge to be key for both parties involved in the processes of education.

Obviously, this is not a novel, where most people start at the beginning and read through to the end. You may want to read a specific chapter to seek ideas to tackle a specific issue. This may lead you to other chapters and thus additional perspectives. When writing this book, I found that this led to some, but not much, overlap.

I worried about the first chapter not being quite as classroom-helpful as the others, but I wanted to take an overview of current and recent information on where we are with maths education – that is, a justification for my own beliefs – and I wanted to follow the advice from Daniel Kahneman on an exaggerated faith in small samples (*Thinking, Fast and Slow*, p. 118).

In this new world of computer technology and search engines, I have not provided a formal list of references, but I have provided enough information in the text for the relevant research to be found on the web.

Please note that this book is not a teaching manual.

15 y 51.0%
16–19 y 49.1%

Having just written y for 'years' in presenting the data above, I shouldn't have been surprised to see this answer to one of the other questions from my test:

$2y + 5 = 31$ $y = $ _____

y = years.
That could be an example of Sharpe's hypothesis.

Initiatives in general

As a teacher in England in the mid-1980s, I experienced SMP, the Schools Mathematics Project. The main components were plastic-coated work cards, which pupils took, completed and returned to the teacher for marking before taking the next card. It was individual learning but with minimum teaching input from teachers.

It was soulless, especially for me as a teacher who really enjoys teaching, but it was used and promoted in many schools.

It should not be surprising that not all initiatives work well. (A long time ago, I realised that 'Nothing works for everyone'.) There are aficionados and enthusiasts, and the occasional snake-oil salesman, to be found somewhere for most things. I used to work on the optimistic principle that rational evaluations outweighed enthusiasms and beliefs. Not always.

Recently in England we have looked at 'Shanghai maths' and have sent teachers to Shanghai to observe and learn. The learning culture for maths in Asia is not the same as the culture in the West. That could make transferring pedagogies challenging. It's always complicated. In January 2019, *Tes*, the teachers' weekly paper in the UK, reported, 'The Department for Education's Shanghai mathematics programme has had little impact on pupil results or attitudes towards maths, an evaluation report shows'.

I vividly remember on my first visit to Singapore being amazed to find maths tutoring centres in many of the many malls. (Apparently, there are now maths tutoring centres in some UK supermarkets.) At first, I thought that this was a subtle indoctrination scheme to put children off shopping. Not so. It is an example of the different maths culture and specifically the attitude to maths in Singapore and Asia.

What is interesting for me is, that back in the 1980s, Singapore used the 'Cockcroft Report on Mathematics in Schools' from the UK and 'An Agenda for Action: Recommendations for School Mathematics in the 1980s' from the National Council of Teachers of Mathematics in the US to support the introduction of problem solving and investigation as a focus for building their new maths curriculum. We didn't. They also made extensive use of Bruner's work.

I did have the privilege of consulting on maths learning difficulties for a week with a great team in Singapore's Ministry of Education.

Initiatives then and now

There are a huge number of books, research papers and articles out there on teaching maths. Ideas can fade away and be brought back into the limelight several years later, a point made in 'Models for teaching mathematics revisited' (Mathematics Teaching, 268,

Sept. 2019). For example, I see a close resemblance between 'precision teaching', introduced in the 1960s, and 'mastery', which is a current approach for some maths educators.

I don't think it's just about my age, although one consequence is that I have seen many ideas come and go, but I do feel we often fail to look back far enough to check whether there is any bit of research or wisdom that might need re-visiting. Or maybe thinking 'Thank goodness we dropped that'.

One of the themes in this book is to look back at ideas and track their re-emergence. The principle is that if they re-emerge then maybe that means they have some validity (for example, mastery). This is not guaranteed for every case.

The 2018 Education Endowment Foundation report 'Improving Mathematics in Key Stages 2 and 3' (for ages 7 to 14) looked at evidence for maths programmes and found:

> Evidence from US studies in the 1980s generally shows mastery approaches to be effective, particularly for mathematics attainment. However, very small effects were obtained when excluding all but the most rigorous studies, carried out over longer time periods. Effects tend to be higher for primary rather than secondary learners and when programmes are teacher-paced, rather than student-paced. The US meta-analyses are focused on two structured mastery programmes, which are somewhat different from the kinds of mastery approaches currently being promoted in England. Only limited evidence is available on the latter, which suggests that, at best, the effects are small. There is a need for more research here.
> Strength of evidence: MEDIUM

The UK's National Centre for Excellence in the Teaching of Mathematics (NCETM) currently advocates using small steps in the teaching of mathematics, sometimes known as precision teaching, which is designed to support pupils in developing accuracy and fluency often using short tasks to build skills by practising them regularly. The NCETM observed that, in China, teachers 'deployed short, precise steps with clear logical progression to develop mathematics'. This is not great for learners with a 'grasshopper' cognitive style (Chapter 7). I saw an example of this during a classroom observation in Hong Kong where the lesson was about plotting a graph for $y = x^2$. It was a very 'inch-worm' (see Chapter 7) lesson. Metacognition should be an important pedagogical component of maths schemes. Small steps are not great for catch-up either.

The pioneering book *Guiding Each Child's Learning of Mathematics* (Ashlock et al.) was published in 1981. It included a structured list of 23 steps for whole number addition. Back in the mid-1980s, I used this list to try out small-step teaching with one of my 14-year-old students with dyslexia, working with him for around five minutes every day. The problem I found was that his ability to retain earlier steps, despite including reviews of previous work, slowed down our progress and the gains we secured were at the expense of a lot of time. This was not a catch-up procedure. It wasn't too motivating either. That book, by the way, was a revelation in how many great ideas and new perspectives it taught me.

The Mathematics Teaching 'revisiting' article draws a conclusion that I could interpret as recognising and acknowledging the diversity of students. They are a truly heterogeneous population. For this one key factor alone, we need to be very wary of restricting pedagogies to a limited model. If we follow the 'small steps, path smoothing' method exclusively, then we risk losing the elements of exploration, challenges and metacognition. Most importantly, we risk not meeting the diverse learning needs of our students, including their short-term and working memory capacities. Again, we must keep in mind that 'Nothing works for everyone'.

I could round this section off by again mentioning the 'curse of knowledge', summed up as 'When you know something, it can be difficult to think about it from the perspective of someone who does not know it'. I have a feeling that this has had too much influence on maths education, hence my philosophy of learning from the outliers. The curse of knowledge scares me and ties in with Daniel Kahneman's observation that 'Even compelling causal statistics will not change long-held beliefs or beliefs rooted in personal experience' (2011). That, in turn, ties in with Key Finding 1 from the US National Research Council book *How People Learn*:

> Students come to the classroom with preconceptions about how the world works. If their initial understanding is not engaged, they may fail to grasp the new concepts and information that they are taught, or they may learn them for the purposes of a test but revert to their preconceptions outside the classroom.

How People Learn (2000) is one of the most influential books I have read. It is research-based and evidence-based. It highlights three findings that have both a solid research base and strong implications for how we teach. I have already quoted Key Finding 1. The other two are:

Key Finding 2

To develop competence in an area of enquiry, students must:

(a) have a deep foundation of factual knowledge,
(b) understand facts and ideas in the context of a conceptual framework, and
(c) organise knowledge in ways that facilitate retrieval and application.

Key Finding 3

A 'metacognitive' approach to instruction can help students learn to take control of their own learning by defining learning goals and monitoring their progress in achieving them.

At the start of this chapter, I wrote about problems with learning maths and low achievement levels. A major contributor to that situation is a difficulty with retaining pertinent information in long-term memory. So (a) in Key Finding 2 can be a challenge for many learners. Hopefully, we can define 'deep knowledge' in a way that is attainable for many learners. What makes Key Finding 2 so key for maths are (b) and (c). The pedagogy for maths needs to include these as essential basics, as 'students must'. I try to illustrate and expand on that principle throughout this book.

Key Finding 3 points me to finding out what students know and how they know it. I think that the best way to do that is to ask them. And listen to the responses, which does require a classroom ethos that encourages all those interchanges to happen. Ask questions such as,

Can you tell me how you did that?
What were you doing here?

And they better be said with the right intonation!

The content of this book is based on research from around the world and decades of my own experience in the classroom. The success of the pedagogy in my school was recognised by the UK Department of Education when they awarded us 'Beacon School' status to enable us to train teachers how to teach maths to students with dyslexia and other students who had maths learning difficulties. I would add, as further evidence of possible efficacy, that I have presented lectures and trained teachers in over 30 countries, often with repeat visits. No one has walked out yet!

Parents

It's worth finding Tom Lehrer's satirical song 'New Math' on the internet. Apart from anything else, it's a warning that every time someone changes the pedagogy of maths, especially the algorithms, many parents are disempowered from helping their children. It shows, in a sardonic way, how the impact of even small changes in an approach or an algorithm can confuse and disempower. Parents can be a positive influence on learning, although when I offered to help my daughter with special needs with maths, prefaced by me explaining how some people considered me an expert (as a persuading strategy rather than a boast), she would say, 'You're my Dad, not my maths teacher'.

Final thoughts

I had taught successfully (so they say) in the first 14 years of my career. This was pre-ceded by three years, whilst working on my doctorate, of successfully teaching 'advanced'-level maths to food science undergraduates who had failed to pass when in school. In 1981, I took a post as head of a new senior school for boys with dyslexia. Part of this role was to teach maths. Suddenly, I was very aware that I was no longer a successful teacher.

No one was running courses for maths learning difficulties back in 1981. Fortunately, I met up with two pioneers from the US, John Bath and Dwight Knox, and in 1984 I took up a one-year post as visiting head of their school in Baltimore, Maryland. We worked together on developing skills for teaching maths to students who had great difficulty in achieving any success. I took special education courses at Johns Hopkins University. I researched (pre-Google) in the university's library. I began to learn that our students *could* be taught maths and I realised that what I was learning about teaching was applicable way further up the learning spectrum. I'm still learning, and pupils still teach me. One of the best examples of this is via an Australian teacher who gave me these wise words from a 10-year-old student:

> I am good at × + and −; divide is sometimes hard. I would love to be a bit better at ÷ and ×. If you want me to be better at maths, you should show me a pattern in it like a rhyme.
>
> I like maths when I get it right. I don't like getting maths wrong. You should show me how to get my errors right, by giving me a strategy.

So my one key learning behind my attempts to write this book is 'What works with students who find maths difficult usually works for most students'. My philosophy then is to improve learners' understandings and thus change maths from being a 'remember this' subject to a 'let's understand this' subject. So, taking the words of a remarkable educator from the US, Dr Margaret Rawson, and applying them to maths, images or materials), but they are habitually taught purely as a memory exercise. The promotion of a dominant reliance on rote learning these facts is deeply embedded in the culture of maths.

The learner does not recognise and use the commutative property for addition and multiplication facts (for example, not recognising that 7 + 5 is the same as 5 + 7 or that 6 × 3 is the same as 3 × 6). Learners who interpret things literally are at risk in maths.

It is not unusual for the learner to know with any fluency only the 2×, 5× and 10× (and 1×) multiplication facts. However, these core facts can be used to access other facts and teach some maths concepts as well (see Chapter 8). This could be interpreted as a similar strategy to using key phonemes to decode words.

Learners may count on to access even these facts. If there is to be a focus on rote learning, then it should be here, with the basics. They will need to have automatic recall of the core facts if they are not to overload working memory when using them to work out other facts. This is my interpretation of the National Research Council Key Finding 2 phrase, 'deep foundation'.

They make 'big' errors for multiplication facts, such as 6 × 7 = 67 or 6 × 7 = 13. In a classroom research study, I found that these errors, rather than, say, mismatching 8 × 7 not with 56 but with another answer from the tables square (say, 54), were more common amongst pupils who knew the least number of facts. This is a worryingly poor sense of number.

The learner fails to 'see' and use the relationships between addition and subtraction facts (such as counting on to subtract) or the relationships between multiplication and division facts. This is another understanding that will be needed later in the maths curriculum.

The learner sees numbers literally and not inter-related with other numbers (for example, when adding 9, counts on 9 rather than adding 10 and subtracting 1). This impacts on developing the skill of estimation.

They do not have strategies to use what they know to work out what they don't know (for example, to work out 12 × 12 as '10 × 12 + 2 × 12' or to use '7 + 7 + 1' to compute 7 + 8).

Place value

An understanding of place value is critical as it is an integral and perseverant part of so many maths topics. It is a classic illustration of the developmental nature of maths. Connie Ho and colleagues (2015) found that, in Hong Kong, a simple place value test given half-way through first grade identified 95% of the children who were low achievers in second grade.

The learner does not understand and therefore is unable to use place value knowledge correctly when doing addition, subtraction, multiplication and division problems.

Zero is often a challenge. For example, learners find it difficult to write numbers that have zeros within them, such as 'forty thousand and twenty-one'.

There is often a problem when multiplying and dividing by powers of 10, especially when this involves decimal numbers. There is often an over-emphasis on the decimal point and 'moving it'.

Renaming/decomposing numbers is a procedural problem often exacerbated by the demand to organise work on paper.

Estimation

This is a key skill and is arguably related to cognitive style. Metacognition is involved here. It is a life skill. A good question in the early stages of teaching estimation is 'Is your estimate bigger or smaller than the accurate answer?' It's hard for students to get this wrong twice for the same example!

The learner does not have the skills, and thus the inclination, for making pre- and post-calculation estimates/appraisals of answers.

The learner sees numbers literally and in isolation. They do not link numbers. For example, they do not see 5% as half of 10% or 97 as 3 less than 100. Number sense can be depressed by this behaviour.

They have little sense of estimation values and answers and avoid this task.

With money, they tend to be literal and selective in their focus. For example, they think an item priced at £14.99 is '£14 and a bit' rather than almost £15. That '.99' is daunting for many people. It's less stressful for them if they ignore it in these contexts rather than rounding up, which changes the £ number.

Some learners prefer to use formulas (in a formulaic way) and procedures, even if they find it difficult to retain them in long-term memory, rather than estimate and refine. They use formulas and procedures mechanically without any understanding of how they work. Indeed, they can be unwilling to make any attempt to try to understand as they perceive this as extending a task that is challenging their endurance! This is also an example of an inflexible cognitive style (see Chapter 7).

When I taught in the US, one of my great students said of his answers when they were not spot-on correct, 'Close enough for government work'. 'Government work' is a shining example of estimation. Usually under-estimation.

Math memories

The obvious example of maths memory is a failure to retrieve basic number facts, especially multiplication facts, from long-term memory and to not have efficient compensatory strategies when recall fails. Learners are probably relieved that we don't often ask for division facts. Even the UK Government doesn't do this (but don't hold your breath).

They forget instructions and questions (a short-term memory problem).

They find mental arithmetic a massive challenge which often induces anxiety and a fear of failure. This is a consequence of insufficient short-term memory to remember the question or the instructions and then an insufficient working memory to calculate an answer, maybe combined with a poor long-term memory for facts and procedures, or all of these. Mental arithmetic is overwhelmingly dependent on memories, so it's a classic example of the question, 'What are you testing?' If you know that memories are weak, why present questions in a way that only confirms that information?

Speed of working

Back to the normal distribution. Many learners will be slow at doing maths or be perceived as slow when judged against the culture of speedy maths. The normal distribution tells us that some will be super-fast. This may not always be a good thing. I had a new student who was good at maths and confident in himself that this was so. I had given the class a basic arithmetic test and he finished extremely quickly. The first four questions were on addition. Unfortunately, he continued adding with all the other questions, even though none of them was about addition. Perseveration. Very little we do in a classroom is simple. We don't teach robots.

Learners work slowly (relative to other students) and may be slow to start work.

This can be for a whole bunch of reasons, such as not being able to find a pen, trying to get the task organised in their head and reluctance based on affective domain issues.

They may not answer several of the questions in an exercise or a test. Refusals/withdrawals are common. Despite this, they consequently attempt fewer questions; often they are still slow to finish working on the task.

They write slowly and their work is poorly organised on the page. (*Squared paper may help.*)

In a comment on their study of a huge sample of young adults in New Zealand, Sharpe and Hughson (personal communication, 2019), reflecting on a massive set of data from their research study, hypothesised that,

> The length of time taken to achieve correct answers dispels the myth that "to be good at maths, you must be fast at maths". Those learners who achieved more highly took longer to calculate the answers. Learners therefore require time to successfully undertake numeracy exercises.

Of course, there are some who simply race through the task just to get it over with.

Poor organisation of work on the page

Some algorithms require good organisation of work on the page (for example, 'long' multiplication and 'long' division). Keeping numbers ordered in place values is essential for obtaining correct answers. Again, squared paper can help. And scaffolding (see Chapter 5).

Anxiety

See Chapter 13.

One of the most dominant errors from my standardised test was the 'no attempt'. I have the data! And I've written the paper! Withdrawal from a task that is perceived as too challenging makes sense to many people. It is a strategy for managing fear of negative evaluation and thus reduces anxiety.

Setting questions that learners don't answer is a pretty futile exercise. It only confirms the learner's opinion that maths is an impossible subject and that they are not going to be able to learn it. Seligman calls this 'learned helplessness'. I call it 'taught helplessness'. Let me sum up this collection of behaviours first, then talk about sequencing and classifying and then return to setting questions.

Noticing, monitoring and diagnosing these problem behaviours

Obviously, intervention that is targeted at an individual's specific problems is going to be more effective. The behaviours listed above help this objective. Ultimately, this is about taking a diagnostic approach to teaching which will include recognising error patterns and knowing the likely causes of these errors. There is a chapter on errors in my diagnosis book, *More Trouble with Maths* (3rd edition).

Although I have just used the word 'individual', many of these behaviours will be common to more than one learner. It's the combination of behaviours that is individual. Ideally, teachers should take a pre-emptive approach to presenting topics that are notorious for creating misunderstandings, thus avoiding those very influential erroneous first learning experiences. It's unlikely to be just one learner who benefits. It's about maximising communication and learning in the classroom and about aiming for the whole class with positive differentiation. For me it's a massive challenge. I'm still working at it but at least I've started. There are a couple of aspects of this that I will discuss later. I think my favourite word here is *Einstellung*. As I said, 'Later'.

Who started long before me?

Once again, I bring in that 'I've been around a long time' thing. One of the first books I read on learning difficulties had the great title, *No Easy Answers* (Sally Smith, 1978). It was published by the US Department of Health, Education and Welfare over 40 years ago. Sally Smith wrote this list of 'Some Typical Arithmetic Problems':

1. Counts on his fingers.
2. Cannot commit multiplication facts to memory.
3. Reverses two place numbers – 13 becomes 31. Also reverses 5, etc.
4. Doesn't understand place value.
5. May solve addition and even multiplication problems by counting on fingers but cannot subtract, which is the reverse operation.
6. Subtracts the smaller number in a column from a larger number. In the problem 25 – 7, he subtracts the 5 from the 7 simply because the 5 is smaller.
7. Often understands concepts but can't do it in written, symbolic form with paper and pencil.
8. On the other hand, sometimes a child can do rote arithmetic on paper, but it has no meaning and he can't solve problems in daily life, such as making change.
9. Can't remember a sequence of steps to multiply or divide. Has trouble in switching from one process to another, such as dividing and subtracting in long division.
10. Solves problems left to right instead of right to left (directional issues).

I have to ask, maybe without expecting an explanation, why has this not yet permeated maths education, some 40 years later, and helped us teach the 'learners as they are'? Why do we see these same errors 40 years on?

Sequencing, classifying and understanding number

This is another example of ideas and concepts that were written about many years ago and then picked up again recently and acknowledged as significant factors for learning maths. The 'then and now' researchers both point to the critical role these skills play in learning maths (for example, seriation being used in putting fractions on a number line or classification used in collecting like terms in algebra).

In 1941, Piaget and Szeminska suggested that there was a relationship between seriation, the logical ability to sort objects on the basis of differences while ignoring similarities, and classification, the logical ability to sort objects on the basis of similarities while ignoring differences, and the understanding of number.

In 2015, Desoete suggested that seriation and classification (as logical thinking skills) combined with procedural and conceptual counting knowledge are significant predictive indicators for mathematical learning disabilities in kindergarten.

They are pervasive skills in learning maths and thus behaviours around these skills should be noticed and addressed. Sometimes, I think we hope learners pick up these skills by osmosis, but I believe they deserve overt teaching.

Generalising and patterns

There is enough evidence out there to recognise that many learners have difficulty in remembering maths information. I also have a suspicion that sometimes, maybe too often, maths is taught on a 'remember this' principle (that is, rote learning). Maybe that's more than a suspicion. This goes alongside another suspicion that some learners collude with this approach, having little interest in trying to understand maths.

However, maths is a great subject for generalising and patterns. These two skills can be used to support memory by linking facts and concepts and by giving them some rationale (for example, in algebra, collecting like terms and, in basic facts, by seeing the linking pattern for adding 10 and adding 9).

Chapter 3

The core curriculum for arithmetic

I shall focus on arithmetic or the study of number because that's where maths education starts and where learners first experience failure. I think that the arithmetic content of most primary curricula is pretty much self-evident and self-selecting and is essentially predictable in the way skills are ordered. What's often left to tweak is the general pace of learning, although this is not always possible for teachers to control when curricula topics are set in time allocations.

Usually, a curriculum is light on methodology, so what I want to explore are the topics we teach, and the way they are developed, so that we can recognise efficacious teaching strategies and ways to make maths as accessible as possible to as many learners as possible. Maths is very developmental (see also Chapter 4), so I plan to set out a typical primary curriculum in a developmental way to show where a particular topic comes from and how it got there and thus highlight where gaps in learning and understanding are likely to create problems as the curriculum progresses. This is an important awareness for teachers.

This knowing where a topic or a concept has come from and where it's heading can help learners to link concepts. So I have presented the maths curriculum for the first four primary years in reverse order. My main reason for doing this is to show the structure more clearly and thus how far back to go to start intervention. My experience is that it is usually much further back than we might at first think.

Building links between different topics and concepts is important, too. That depends on supporting understanding rather than allowing confusion with seemingly unrelated topics to breed more confusion.

One recurring theme throughout this book is the importance of first experiences of new topics. Whatever a learner learns when first experiencing a new topic becomes a dominant entry to the brain unless inhibited or unlearned. There is enough established research to support this, dating back to Buswell and Judd in 1925, Luchins in 1942 (who introduced me to the wonderfully sounding word, *Einstellung*), the National Research Council (US) in 2000 and more recently with 'inhibition'.

I reckon many of you reading this book can think of examples from everyday life where this erroneous first learning has happened to you. That first learning experience is hard to overrule in the brain. A curriculum leads to smooth progress only if it builds on correct and secure understandings. What a great research topic for the neuropsychologists.

I've taken a typical curriculum for arithmetic and, instead of structuring it as the whole arithmetic curriculum for Year 1 and then Years 2, 3 and 4, firstly I've restructured it by topics and then I have ordered them in reverse, for Year 4 to Year 1. I often say in my talks that we need to know where a topic comes from (that is, to know its roots). I'm also prone to saying (again and again, as in this book) for intervention, 'Go back further than you might think, maybe even to the beginning'. This 'reverse' structure might make tracking back more accessible.

Pupils in Years 1 and 2 are 5 to 7 years old and in Years 3 and 4 are 7 to 9 years old.

Counting

Year 4. Count in multiples of 6, 7, 9, 25 and 1000. Find 1000 more or less than a given number. Count backwards through zero to include negative numbers. Order and compare numbers beyond 1000.

Year 3. Count from 0 in multiples of 4, 8, 50 and 100. Find 10 or 100 more or less than a given number. Compare and order numbers up to 1000. Read and write numbers up to 1000 in numerals.

Year 2. Count in steps of 2, 3 and 5 from 0 and in tens from any number, forward and backward. Use the number line to compare and order numbers from 0 up to 100. Write numbers to at least 100 in numerals and in words.

Year 1. Count to and across 100, forwards and backwards, beginning with 0 or 1 or from any given number. Count, read and write numbers to 100 in numerals. Count in multiples of twos, fives and tens. Given a number, identify one more and one less. Identify and represent numbers using objects and pictorial representations, including the number line, and write numbers from 1 to 20 in numerals and words.

Some observations

This is the most straightforward topic in the primary curriculum. Nevertheless, there are some areas where teachers should be looking out for difficulties. Counting backwards is an important skill, as is reversing any procedure, but some children will find it a difficult task. Counting on in steps of 2, 5 and 10 follows quite predictable patterns but this is less so for 3, 4, 6, 7 and 8. Counting on in steps of 9 can be achieved by counting on 10 and subtracting 1, and counting on in 7s can be done in two steps by adding 5 and 2. There are patterns in the sequences for these sub-tasks. Counting on sets the foundation for addition, and counting back the foundation for subtraction.

A difficulty with being able to count backwards is often an indicator of potential problems in maths. It can overload working memory. Materials and visuals can help learners to see the patterns and develop confidence rather than confusion. Being able to reverse sequences and procedures is a key skill for being good at maths.

There is, of course, a strong link in this topic to place value. We need to keep in mind that very few skills exist in isolation.

Number: Addition and subtraction

Year 4. Add and subtract numbers with up to four digits using the formal written methods of columnar addition and subtraction. Where appropriate, estimate and use inverse operations to check answers to a calculation. Solve addition and subtraction two-step problems in contexts, deciding which operations and methods to use and why.

Year 3. Add and subtract numbers mentally, including a three-digit number and ones, a three-digit number and tens, and a three-digit number and hundreds. Add and subtract numbers with up to three digits, using formal written methods of columnar addition and subtraction. Estimate the answer to a calculation and use inverse operations to check answers. Solve problems, including missing number problems, using number facts, place value, and more complex addition and subtraction.

Year 2. Solve problems with addition and subtraction, using concrete objects and pictorial representations. Apply their increasing knowledge of mental and written methods. Recall and use addition and subtraction facts to 20 fluently. Derive and use related facts up to 100. Add and subtract numbers using concrete objects, pictorial representations and mentally. This includes a two-digit number and ones, a two-digit number and tens, and two two-digit numbers. Add three one-digit numbers. Show that addition of two numbers can be done in any order (commutative) and that subtraction of one number from another cannot. Recognise and use the inverse relationship between addition and subtraction and use this to check calculations and solve missing number problems.

Year 1. Read, write and interpret mathematical statements involving addition (+), subtraction (–) and equals (=) signs. Represent and use number bonds and related subtraction facts within 20. Add and subtract one-digit and two-digit numbers to 20, including zero. Solve one-step problems that involve addition and subtraction, using concrete objects and pictorial representations, and missing number problems such as $7 = ? - 9$.

Some observations

Symbols, + − = are introduced. This will inevitably create problems for some pupils. The language used around these symbols should initially be consistent until the concepts are secure. The range of words then can be introduced. Zero is mentioned in Year 1. Zero often challenges learners, especially as the curriculum develops, so early exposure combined with understanding will be key to future learning.

The missing number problem used as an illustration in Year 2 ($7 = ? - 9$) is a challenging format and so is maybe not the best example to choose. I use that format for a question in my 15-minute standardised test because it is a challenge. The gradation of difficulty of examples used to introduce number problems is important. Pupils do not need to be over-faced by early examples. *It might help to make 7 = ? – 9 into a word problem and use the bar model method and Cuisenaire rods to illustrate it.*

Estimation is a key skill, but literal learners will find it challenging. Concrete objects and appropriate visuals can help. Awareness of the inverse relationship between addition and subtraction is another key factor. This is introduced, appropriately early, in Year 2. Deriving facts from related facts is another key skill that will help pupils retrieve facts that are not embedded in long-term memory.

Year 3 gives some prominence to mental arithmetic with the end objective of 'adding a three-digit number and hundreds'. I give quite a bit of attention to mental arithmetic in this book, most of it critical (for good reasons, of course). At my lectures, I have asked (by now) thousands of teachers, 'At what age do enough children in class give up on maths for you to notice?' The modal answer is 7 years old. So we need to look at the curriculum for pupils around this age and identify the causes – and address them with pupils' learning profiles in mind because we can't just remove those topics and concepts from the curriculum. That is not helpful for developing maths skills and understandings.

Written methods require good skills in organising work on paper. Squared paper may help some learners.

The number bonds for 10 can be useful for adding columns of numbers. The strategy is to look down the columns and cross out any combination of numbers that add to make 10 rather than mechanically adding in the sequence given.

Number: Multiplication and division

Year 4. Recall multiplication and division facts for multiplication tables up to 12×12. Use place value and known and derived facts to multiply and divide mentally, including multiplying by 0 and 1 and dividing by 1. Multiplying together three numbers. Recognise and use factor pairs and commutativity in mental calculations. Multiply two-digit and three-digit numbers by a one-digit number using a formal written layout. Solve problems involving multiplying and adding, including using the distributive law to multiply two-digit numbers by one-digit numbers. Integer scaling problems and harder correspondence problems such as n objects are connected to m objects.

   Year 3. Recall and use multiplication and division facts for the 3, 4 and 8 multiplication tables. Write and calculate mathematical statements for multiplication and division using the multiplication tables that they know, including for two-digit numbers times one-digit numbers. Use mental methods and progress to formal written methods. Solve problems, including missing number problems, involving multiplication and division, and including positive integer scaling problems and correspondence problems in which n objects are connected to m objects.

   Year 2. Recall and use multiplication and division facts for the 2, 5 and 10 multiplication tables, including recognising odd and even numbers. Calculate mathematical statements for multiplication and division within the multiplication tables and write them using the multiplication ($\times$), division ($\div$) and equals ($=$) signs. Show that multiplication of two numbers can be done in any order (commutative) and that division of one number by another cannot. Solve problems involving multiplication and division, using materials, arrays, repeated addition, mental methods, and multiplication and division facts, including problems in contexts.

   Year 1. Solve one-step problems involving multiplication and division by calculating the answer using concrete objects, pictorial representations and arrays with the support of the teacher. (*I think it may be a tad more complicated than that at this age. And the support materials must be automatically linked to the symbols in the learner's mind.*)

Observations

The quantum leaps in Years 3 and 4 are noticeable. For example, the multiplication and division facts demanded in Year 3 are for 3, 4 and 8. There are straightforward strategies for these, using 3 as $2 + 1$ and 4 as 2×2 and 8 as $2 \times 2 \times 2$ (working memory permitting). Then in Year 4, facts to 12×12 are required. I used to say in my lectures that '12×12 is gross', but the younger teachers didn't know what I meant mathematically by 'gross'. Gross should be irrelevant in 2020 maths. And we are now pretty much metric in the UK. A cricketer's ambition (could a cricketer have a 'goal'?) may be to score a century. I've never heard that it's to score a gross. It's not worth spending time rote learning this when the $10\times$ plus $2\times$ strategy does the job. Year 4 includes 'using the distributive law to multiply two-digit numbers by one-digit numbers' without including the use of this strategy to work out 'facts' such as 12×8.

   The distributive law and partial products are key concepts as multiplication and division progress.

   More symbols ($\times$ and $\div$) are introduced and thus the vocabulary that accompanies them.

   The links between operations are mentioned in Year 2, where multiplication is related to repeated addition. The link is not made between division and repeated subtraction.

Year 2 mentions 'mental methods' but without expanding on how these are related to, and maybe support, written methods.

The number of digits involved in tasks increases in Years 3 and 4, predictably, but maybe at some stage in this progression pupils begin to think that maths is no longer for them. Working memory could well be a factor here, especially for mental arithmetic. The use of materials is not mentioned in Years 3 and 4. I think that is too soon to abandon these supports for learning.

Fractions

Year 4. Recognise and show, using diagrams, families of common equivalent fractions. Count up and count down in hundredths. Recognise that hundredths arise when dividing an object by one hundred and dividing tenths by ten. Solve problems involving increasingly harder fractions to calculate quantities, and fractions to divide quantities, including non-unit fractions where the answer is a whole number. Add and subtract fractions with the same denominator. Recognise and write decimal equivalents of any number of tenths or hundredths. Recognise and write decimal equivalents to 1/4, 1/2 and 3/4. Find the effect of dividing a one- or two-digit number by 10 and 100, identifying the value of the digits in the answer as ones, tenths and hundredths. Round decimals with one decimal place to the nearest whole number. Compare numbers with the same number of decimal places up to two decimal places. Solve simple measure and money problems involving fractions and decimals to two decimal places.

Year 3. Count up, and count down, in tenths. *(How many of your pupils have counted 'point 8, point 9, point 10'? Scaffolding with place value columns should help avoid this.)* Recognise that tenths arise from dividing an object into 10 equal parts and in dividing one-digit numbers by 10. Recognise, find and write fractions of a discrete set of objects. Unit fractions and non-unit fractions with small denominators. Recognise and use fractions as numbers. Unit fractions and non-unit fractions with small denominators. Recognise and show, using diagrams, equivalent fractions with small denominators. Add and subtract fractions with the same denominator within one whole (for example, 5/7 + 1/7 = 6/7). Compare and order unit fractions and fractions with the same denominators. Solve problems that involve all of the above.

Year 2. Recognise, find, name and write fractions 1/3, 1/4, 2/4 and 3/4 of a length, shape, set of objects or quantity. Write simple fractions (for example, 1/2 of 6 = 3) and recognise the equivalence of 2/4 and 1/2.

Year 1. Recognise, find and name a half as one of two equal parts of an object, shape or quantity. Recognise, find and name a quarter as one of four equal parts of an object, shape or quantity. *(It's hard to cut a pizza or birthday cake into two mathematically equal halves. These are estimation tasks.)*

Observations

The quantum leap is obvious just from the space allocated to fractions in Years 3 and 4. Again, when I lecture, I often ask teachers which maths topics are considered 'too hard' by the pupils. Fractions and division are pretty much always up there! And there is a strong link between the two topics, which is not overtly made in this typical curriculum. So two top hates live together!

Division facts for 4 are not in the curriculum until Year 3, but quarters make their debut, in digit form, in Year 2. It might be a good opportunity to show how to do this by dividing by 2 twice.

Whilst materials are mentioned in Years 1 and 2, there is no explicit mention of using visuals and materials in a developmental way, so that the same models help to develop the understanding of fractions to develop in learners (see Chapter 5).

It's important to link fractions and decimals. Decimals extend the concept of place value and are much easier to place on a number line than fractions. Seigler (2015) and his colleagues suggest that the ability to place fractions on a number line is the key indicator of understanding (see Chapter 12). The link between fractions and decimals is key to that goal.

One of the main problems with fractions is that equivalent fractions can confuse, both as a concept and as a computation exercise. It's those multiplication facts again. The names 'denominator' and 'numerator' can act as barriers to learning. They are confusingly similar. Multiplying by a fraction (less than 1) makes for a smaller answer against previous experience of multiplying making for a bigger answer. The division symbol in fractions is hidden; for example, we write ¾, which means 3 ÷ 4. I worked with an 18-year-old student who would not be convinced that a fraction could have a value above 1. 'Fractions make things smaller'. And for him, 'smaller' in fractions was only for those that were 'less than 1'. In 1/3 of 6, the 'of' still means multiply, but the outcome is a smaller number (2), which challenges previous understandings of 'multiply'.

I saw this in a curriculum document: $\dfrac{1}{3} \div 2 = \dfrac{1}{6}$ set out as I have done here.

It's just so counterintuitive to a whole number brain, especially without visuals to support the answer.

Not surprisingly, I shall be expanding on 'all of the above' throughout this book.

Chapter 4

The developmental nature of maths

In Chapter 3, I set out a typical maths curriculum in a developmental way to show how important the early topics are to become an effectively numerate person. In this chapter, I'm hoping to put some arithmetical flesh on those bones with a focus on one equation and how maths develops that equation.

The power of ab = y

Let's start with a little confusion.

I've used 'power'. Would that have been better if I had started without using 'power' in a non-mathematical sense in a mathematics book? In maths, the meaning of power can be as with the 2 in $y = a^2$. I could have dropped the power word and gone for 'squared' instead but that's too limiting. Maths vocabulary and symbols can confuse. I hope I've just done that (as an example).

OK. Let me be sensible. I want to write about the pervasiveness in early maths of the many manifestations and developments of the equation $y = ab$.

It is one of the conventions and the rules of algebra that learners need to recognise and know that

ab is, in fact, 'a times b'. We don't write a × b. Similarly, learners need to know that $\frac{a}{b}$ is a ÷ b.

Now, they may have related this division bit of algebra to fractions where, for example,

$$\frac{7}{10} = 7 \div 10.$$

Sometimes, the symbols – in these two cases, the symbols for operations, the symbols that tell you what to do – are not there. You need to know that really they are there, and you need to know when to look for them not being there when they're not there.

That's that potential for confusion dealt with. Well, maybe the use of letters in $y = ab$ has also created some confusion or maybe stress. I was working on an informal diagnosis with a 15-year-old student and wrote some algebra equation on a piece of paper. 'Oh no! You're using those letters. I don't do letters in maths'.

But the main goal of this chapter is to show just how dependent algebra is on arithmetic and, as ever in maths, how important it is to understand the foundations and the subsequent developments. And algebra teaches about generalising.

It's so often about 'early maths'.

Where does y = ba start? (That's an example of the commutative property.)

It starts with times tables, the multiplication table facts. This is one bit of maths that parents recognise from their school days. Unlike many of the other topics in maths, no curriculum innovator has devised a new and confusing method for explaining and presenting these facts, usually in a way that is logical only to him. So 8×6 still equals 48 and pupils are expected to learn such facts by rote, just as it was when the parents were at school. It seems remarkable to me that many a Minister of Education has backed the need, in their perception (which unfortunately carries weight and influence), for students to *rote* learn the whole body of facts that make up the times tables. 'I learned them. It was good for me and it will be good for you. And you will have to answer any fact quickly. I think 6 seconds is enough for any child'. Samples of one are not a great basis for dictating pedagogy.

In the UK, any time now (2020), Year 4 pupils will have to answer a bunch of times table facts questions, quickly and up to 12×12. I thought the everyday need for the base-12 system has gone – except for time. But then we don't say, 'I'll meet you in a couple of dozen hours' rather than 'Same time tomorrow'. And, as I said before, my (rather sad) gross joke falls flat these days.

Recently, the UK Education Minister responsible for those new tests for times table facts for primary pupils in England refused on television to answer a multiplication question. He was asked 'What is eight times nine?' But the school standards minister said to the presenters: 'I'm not going to get into this. I've learned through bitter experience never to answer these kinds of questions on live television'. One of his predecessors, an economics graduate, answered 7×8 as 54 on his first attempt. If these education top dogs had been shown how to work out these facts rather than rely on fallible memories, they may have been more willing to answer and more successfully; 7×8 comes from 5×8 plus 2×8, so $40 + 16$ and thus 56. And, another strategy, 8×9 is 8 less than 8×10, so $80 - 8 = 72$. (Think of comparing 'ten lots of 8' with '9 lots of 8' and, to check, the digits in the answer, 7 and 2, must add up to 9.)

Wouldn't it be great if students could say in an exam, 'I've learned through experience never to answer questions about times table facts'. The reality is that many students do this even if they don't articulate their reasons.

As a reminder, the key information and ideas behind this book are based largely on what I have learned from listening and watching students who find maths difficult, to the point of its seeming to be impossible, and my belief that they can be applied to most learners. That experience started for me with times table facts.

Failing to memorise and quickly retrieve the times table facts is often pupils' first experience of persistent failure. Finger counting can help with addition facts but it is not anything like as effective with multiplication facts. It's a problem that extends far beyond the 25% figure for innumeracy in adults and the 5% of students who are considered, by research, to have dyscalculia. For many years now, I have been asking the teachers at my lectures, 'What percentage of pupils aged 10 years, in your experience, do not know all their times table facts?' (Since when did this collection of facts become *their* times tables?) The modal answer is 70%. Now that could be an argument for more drilling, more singing the facts, more creative stories about 'thirsty sixes' (36) or 'sick on the floor' (64) but maybe not. 'Sick on the floor', maybe after being a 'thirsty six', is not developmental and not of any diagnostic value.

So to show that, before I was faced with pupils who had learning difficulties with maths, I too lived in ignorance about what my pupils could learn. Here is a confession. In my first week in special education, teaching maths to my new class of 13-year-old students with dyslexia, I quickly discovered that they did not know the times table facts. So I decided that we would start each maths lesson with five minutes of rote learning these facts. Within a week, I could sense that they were starting to hate maths, and me, but not necessarily in that order. On the Friday as I said to them, with great positivity in my voice, 'It's times table time!', one boy got up and banged his head against the wall. My best mate is a professor in behavioural psychology. I had picked up enough insight from him to know that this was a sign of distress. Perceptive to a fault, I changed my approach. It took a while to get it right.

Among other learnings for me here was the obvious one that a lesson should not begin with something many pupils can't do and maybe that they also hate. Luckily, I was exonerated, I think, by the government that some years later (my story was from 1981) decided that each maths lesson in primary school should begin with mental arithmetic, something many pupils find very difficult and come to hate. So that's OK. Government approval for starting lessons with what's impossible and often demotivating for many children.

Here is one last observation before I do some maths. This rote learning business can create disharmony and disappointment in families. If I could have a dollar for every parent or teacher who said to me, 'She learned them last night, but she had forgotten them by the next morning', I would be rich by now. Sharing an activity that results in persistent failure is not a bonding activity. And does calling it 'the fun way to learn' help? Or the 'quick' way? Or the 'easy' way?

Calling something a learner can't do 'easy' does not give a good message.

Learning the times table facts, from 1 × 0 to 10 × 10.

I published a book, *What to do When You Can't Learn Your Times Tables*, in 1996. You can still get it from SEN Books. It's not about rote learning or fun, except maybe the fun of success.

For me, one of the main principles for learning is taken from that book, *How People Learn*, researched and written for the National Research Council (NRC) in the US and published in 2000. (I've mentioned it before.) It has three Key Findings. This is Key Finding 2 (again):

To develop competence in an area of enquiry, students must:

(a) *have a deep foundation of factual knowledge,*
(b) *understand facts and ideas in the context of a conceptual framework, and*
(c) *organise knowledge in ways that facilitate retrieval and application.*

From my experience and perspective, maths is *the* subject for using (b) and (c). That (c) could have been written especially for students who have problems with retrieval. Maybe it was. Certainly by 2000 I, too, had found this to be so efficacious in every way.

So back to my experiences. I found that talking with my students was rewarding in so many ways. Especially the listening bit (that's me doing the listening). One thing I asked them, and every potential student whom I interviewed for a place in my school, was 'Which times tables do you reckon you're good at? Which ones do you reckon you are comfortable with?' You'll notice that I didn't ask them to answer specific facts. I wanted them to want to come to my school.

Inevitably, the answer was 'I know my 2s, 5s and 10s'. Some would add, 'My 1s and 0s'. Well, after flirting with self-voice echo (see Lane and Chinn, 1986), I decided that if this is what I had to work with, I'd work with it.

And the catch-22 of catch-up was always in my mind: How do pupils who go slower catch up?

By now, I had learned to ask myself, 'What else are you teaching?' That is a key question when you view maths as developmental. It can, and should, make teaching more efficacious. It also is a partial explanation for me writing Chapters 1, 2 and 3.

One of the intervention styles you see when you search 'Learning multiplication facts' on the web is to focus on number/symbol patterns rather than materials and visual images. Now, that's OK if your students have a strong number sense, but not so good if they don't. Making the assumption that the relevant prerequisite knowledge is there can be dangerous. At any stage in maths.

So one key component of teaching maths for me is to use and extend what is there, as suggested by NRC Key Finding 2. And to use visual images to emphasise and reinforce the links and to revise and top up basic number sense. It is not my goal in this book to provide detailed explanations of how to address the whole basic maths curriculum. So what follows are some illustrations and explanations of the approach. More details can be found in my other books and resources (see Appendix 2). These examples are very much about 'What else are you teaching?' And revisiting and reviewing.

Tough fact 1. $7 \times 6 = 42$. I think that this fact could be even tougher than 7×8. Must try that out on an Education Minister.

Pre-knowledge:

Multiplication is repeated addition (of the same number). Obviously, this links the operations of addition and multiplication. 'Lots of' is the appropriate linking vocabulary here.

I like to link numbers and to see other numbers in numbers, especially the ones that learners are more familiar with. So

$7 = 5 + 2$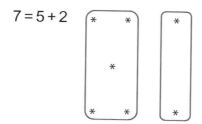

This is also a simple visual link.

Then use two 'key' facts, $5 \times 6 = 30$ and $2 \times 6 = 12$ (preferably with automatic recall … you have to know some facts with automatic retrieval to reduce the load on working memory).

Next the verbalisation: 7 lots of 6 is '5 lots of 6' plus '2 lots of 6'. Thus, $30 + 12 = 42$. The maths behind this is:

$7 \times 6 = 6 + 6 + 6 + 6 + 6 + 6 + 6 = 6 + 6 + 6 + 6 + 6 \ + \ 6 + 6.$

$7 \times 6 = 5 \times 6 + 2 \times 6 = (5 + 2) \times 6 \ (\text{the distributive law}).$

$7 \times 6 = 30 + 12 = 42.$

It may help to show this with Cuisenaire rods. This also links 7×6 to area.

I like this procedure of chunking into partial products. Partial products are developmental, for example, in long multiplication and in algebra.

Under 'What else are you teaching? or 'What else are you setting the foundations for?', this method can be used to work out other facts, such as:

$$3a = (2a + a)$$

$$6a = (5a + a)$$

$$12a = (10a + 2a)$$

$$15a = (10a + 5a)$$

$$19a = (20a - a)$$

and others where the number can be chunked into 1s, 2s, 5s or 10s.

Professor Mahesh Sharma makes a link between using phonemes to help readers to decode words and using core facts to build number facts. Build words, build number facts.

This strategy can be developed into 'long' multiplication, using partial products (for example, 27×48).

Find the core numbers in 27: $27 = 20 + 2 + 5$.

$$27 \times 48 = 20 \times 48 \quad + \quad 2 \times 48 \quad + \quad 5 \times 48.$$

You could, when teaching this, mention and review place value for 2×48 and 20×48.

Tough fact 2. 9×7(without using fingers)

I've seen pupils using a finger method here where they fold down the pertinent finger (say, the seventh one) and then count the fingers on each side. During this process, for some learners, and especially likely for those with developmental coordination disorder (dyspraxia), the seventh finger pops up and the method fails. Nothing works for everyone.

Pre-knowledge:

Multiplication is repeated addition (of the same number).

$9 = 10 - 1$

compared with

10 is a close estimate for 9. So 10×7 is a good (high) estimate for 9×7.

Again, you could use Cuisenaire rods to compare these two multiplications.

Then use '9 lots of seven is 10 lots of seven minus 1 lot of seven'.

Use $10 \times 7 = 70$ and $1 \times 7 = 7$ (again, preferably with automatic recall).

9 lots of 7 in 10 lots of 7 minus 1 lot of 7.

$10 \times 7 - 1 \times 7 = 70 - 7 = 63.$

The digits in the answer, 63, should add up to make 9. Works for any number times 9. I always try to encourage some sort of check of any answer whenever possible.

Tough fact 3. 4×7

Pre-knowledge:

Being able to multiply by 2, to double.

This is a two-step method, so working memory is involved. So the more automatically the key fact is retrieved (x2), the less the load on working memory.

Step 1. $2 \times 7 = 14$

Step 2. $2 \times 14 = 28$

Sometimes, it is helpful to take two easy steps rather than one hard unreachable one. The outcome can be quicker and more accurate. It takes practice and reviews.

A mention of 'being almost right'

Unless you're estimating, being 'almost right' won't do. You don't get a smaller tick. You get a cross. Red is a pretty good colour for demotivational marking, especially if it is from a broad tip pen.

What students do when they don't know the right answer: An interesting lesson for teachers and parents

Back in 2003, I carried out a classroom study of (12-year-old) dyslexic students from my school and two other specialist schools, plus some mainstream students from four schools. I gave them multiplication facts as a multiple-choice exercise. I selected six 'possible' alternative answers, based on experience of predictable errors, and the right answer (seemed fair).

The more errors a student made, the more random and varied the errors. When you haven't a clue, you haven't a clue.

My starting hypothesis was that the most likely error would be a 'mismatch', such as $7 \times 6 = 48$. The student hears the question and makes a connection to a plausible answer in the tables square in their brain, but sadly not the correct one.

Students with dyslexia, 29.6%

Mainstream, 31.8%

Not a big difference.

My colleague's starting hypothesis was for 'close answers' (for example, $7 \times 8 = 58$).

Students with dyslexia, 35.5%

Mainstream, 24.4%.

I never worked out why this was a bigger difference.

For a 'digits' answer, such as $4 \times 5 = 45$:

>   Students with dyslexia, 27.0%
>   Mainstream, 28.1%.

These close results for the two samples are a little bit more evidence for my main hypothesis. There is a normal distribution for most things in teaching. Learning maths for mainstream students is not that different from students with dyslexia, dyscalculia or maths LD, just on a different place in the distribution. Extrapolate up.

Interesting results for addition facts were found by Gray and Tall in 1994. Their study highlighted the use of strategies to compensate for an inability to retrieve facts from memory. They related these to achievement levels in mathematics. In a study of 72 students who were 7 to 13 years old and the ways they accessed addition facts, they found a contrast between the above-average and below-average (at mathematics) students; that is, their groups were distinguished by ability at maths.

For the above-average students:

>   9% counted on.
>   0% counted all.
>   30% recalled facts.
>   61% derived facts, using strategies other than counting.

For the below-average students:

>   72% counted on.
>   22% counted all.
>   6% recalled facts.
>   0% derived facts.

Thus, 94% of the below-average students were dependent on counting to access basic facts such as $6 + 7$. They had no other strategies to access these facts.

The use of strategies was linked to achievement levels. That seems to be an important link.

Where does ab = y go?

I'm showing this visually, using area. You could use base-ten blocks for a lot of these examples to create a kinaesthetic dimension. As ever, the teaching should lead children through the (Bruner) progression from the concrete to the visual to the symbols, although I do think that it is important to make the link to symbols overt at each stage. And back-track when necessary. As ever, ask questions, such as 'How have I changed this example compared to the last one?' or 'What's this bit here mean/represent?'

These illustrations are not a script. It will be those pertinent, low-stress, developmental, metacognitive questions that will make the learning accessible for all students. This is about building and developing concepts and understanding.

A sequence like this helps to show students, and remind them about, the foundations of each new development. Frequent reviews and revisits generally help to secure the concepts.

You'll notice I'm heading to algebra. A lot of students associate algebra with 'Find y', but a key characteristic is using it for generalising, seeing patterns and formalising. These are not always well-developed and secure skills in students with maths difficulties. But they are essential skills for maths in general. The diagrams should help to illustrate examples of generalising. Sometimes, development can result from an overt reflection back to earlier work.

And we must remember that algebra is rooted in arithmetic. Without an understanding of arithmetic, algebra is going to be very difficult.

But I noticed from my many years of teaching that some of my students found algebra more successful than arithmetic. Maybe because there is less emphasis on recalling those basic facts and more on showing what you understand.

I have included a series of diagrams, Figures 4.1 to 4.15, all based on area and thus $y = ab$, to illustrate a developmental strand in maths. In Chapter 3, I set out developmental maths by tracing a typical curriculum backwards to show where topics originate.

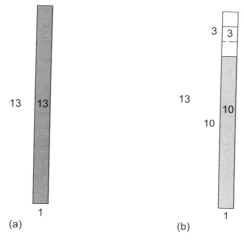

Figure 4.1 (a) Area = 1 × 13 = 13. (b) Area = 1 × 10 + 1 × 3 = 13.

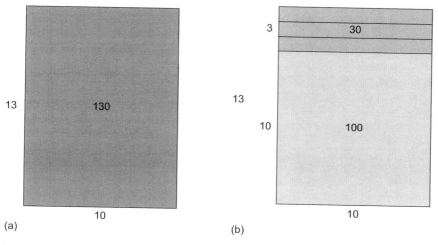

Figure 4.2 (a) Area = 10 × 13 = 130. (b) Area = 10 × 10 + 10 × 3 = 100 + 30 = 130.

You will notice that my illustrations here, and throughout this book, do not include cartoon figures or such distracting frivolity. Boring? Maybe, but I'm hoping this makes it easier to focus on understanding. Perhaps, for younger pupils, lessons could start with the animals and then move on to just symbols? Sort of Bruner. Although it is harder to herd, say, 7 squirrels into a group of 5 and a group of 2 as in my patterns for the 7 example earlier in this chapter. It's a tough life being a classroom squirrel.

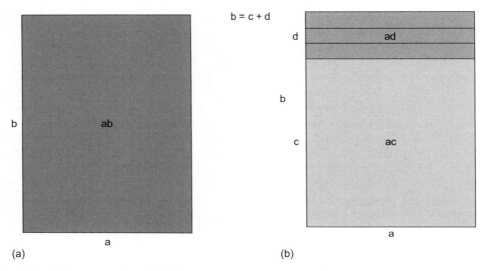

(a)   (b)

Figure 4.3 (a) Area = a × b = ab. (b) Area = a × c + a × d = ac + ad.

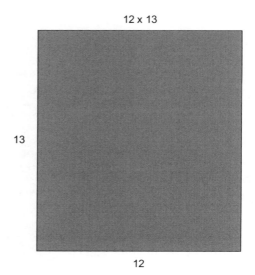

Figure 4.4 Area = 12 × 13.

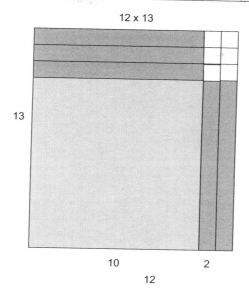

Figure 4.5 Area = $10 \times 10 + 2 \times 10 + 10 \times 3 + 2 \times 3$.

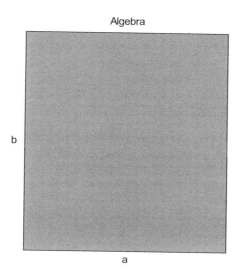

Figure 4.6 Area = $a \times b = ab$.

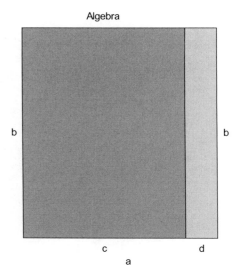

Figure 4.7 Area = cb + db.

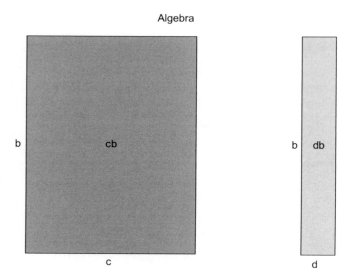

Figure 4.8 Area = cb + db.

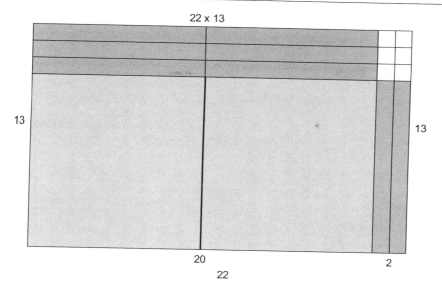

Figure 4.9 Area $= 20 \times 10 + 20 \times 3 + 2 \times 10 + 2 \times 3.$

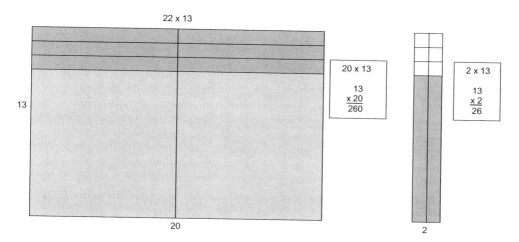

Figure 4.10 Area $= 200 + 60 + 20 + 6 = 260 + 26.$

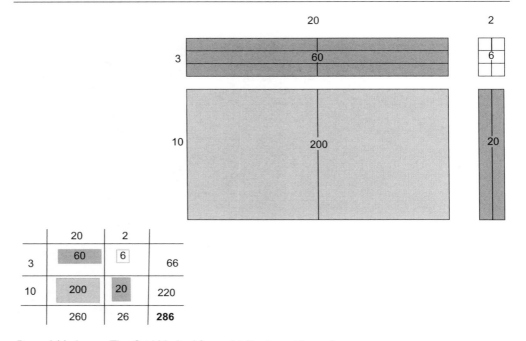

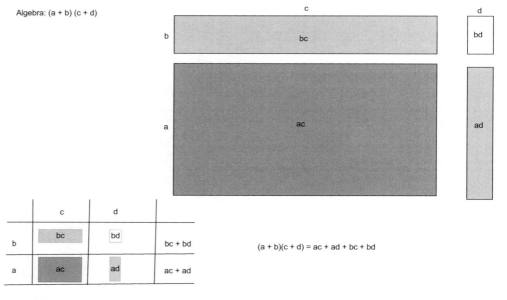

	20	2	
3	60	6	66
10	200	20	220
	260	26	**286**

Figure 4.11 Area = The Grid Method for multiplication with numbers.

Algebra: (a + b) (c + d)

	c	d	
b	bc	bd	bc + bd
a	ac	ad	ac + ad

(a + b)(c + d) = ac + ad + bc + bd

Figure 4.12 Area = The Grid Method for multiplication with algebra.

Using brackets: From 7 x 7 to (a + b)(c + d)

Brackets ...   ( ) ...   are used for two purposes in algebra:

1) to collect together terms

2) to mean multiply

7 x 7 = 7 x (5 + 2) = 7 x 5 + 7 x 2

7x 7 = (5 x 2) x (5 + 2)

= 5 x 5 + 5 x 2   = 25 + 10 = 35

= 2 x 5 + 2 x 2   = 10 + 4 = 14

= 49

(a + b) x (c + d)

= ac + ad

= bc + bd

= ac + ad + bc + ad

Figure 4.13 Procedural multiplication.

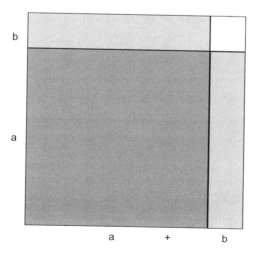

Figure 4.14 Area = $(a + b)^2 = (a + b)(a + b)$.

$(a + b)^2$

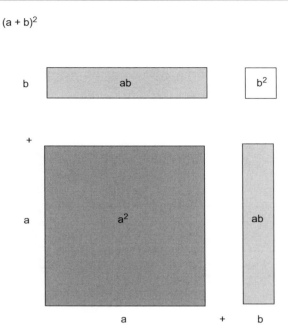

Figure 4.15 Area $= a^2 + ab + ab + b^2 = a^2 + 2ab + b^2$.

Figures 4.1 to 4.15. Developing $y = ab$. A model using area to illustrate the equation. Each Figure relates to the equation in the caption.

Summing up

When a student has fallen behind in maths, it is very hard for them to catch up. One obvious reason that they are behind is that they work more slowly than average. To catch up, they will need to work faster, or more effectively than average, which is not something teachers can just demand.

Gurus, such as Professor David Geary, warn us about the long-term impact of early failure.

> Children who start school without a solid understanding of number words, numerals, and the quantities they represent are at heightened risk for poor mathematics achievement throughout schooling and, as a result, poor employment-relevant quantitative skills.

Structures such as this one for $ab = y$ create opportunities to frequently revisit foundations and relate them to new developments so that they have a stronger meaning. This allows us to move maths away from a total reliance on a retrieval of seemingly unrelated, complex and demanding information to an emphasis on understanding. I like to think that knowing 'Why' helps us to remember. So why does 6×7 make 42?

Chapter 5

Topics which cause the most difficulty

Over the many years since I started to specialise in maths learning difficulties, I have lectured and provided training in over 30 countries. I usually ask my audience, 'Which are the topics that your students find most difficult?' So my sample is very large and international but informal. I've gone for 'sample size overrules precision' validation.

The most common answers are 'word problems, fractions, division and learning the basic facts'. I think this overlooks place value. I ask a further question across the UK about times table facts, of which more later. Such data should unite us in seeking solutions that really work long term rather than quirky interventions often based on very small samples, such as one's own children or memories of one's own school days. Unfortunately, or maybe fortunately, this 'own children' thing didn't apply to me. I used to tell my younger daughter, 'Look, I'm a world expert. Let me help you'. (Not my usual style, that 'world expert' bit, but your own kids can be hard to impress.) Her response was 'You're my Dad. I don't want to do maths with you'. Interesting comment. Probably a wise comment.

I have written about word problems and fractions in separate chapters, so my focus in this chapter will be on place value, basic facts and division. As ever, there are many links and interactions between different topics in maths.

Place value

Among the themes running through this book are the links between the many factors involved in learning. I received this email a couple of years ago: 'Steve, it was thanks to your work on maths that I was able to work out what was stopping a new Year 5 in our school from being able to carry out the simplest of calculations. He wrote, $5 + 6 = 1$, "Because when you get to ten you go back to one again, don't you?"'

Place value involves the use of zero. Zero can challenge pupils' understanding of number. For example, I used zeros in several items in my standardised 15-minute test to help achieve a normal distribution for the answers and to probe understanding. These include

$100 - 58$

$$\begin{array}{r} 103 \\ -\ 96 \\ \hline \end{array}$$

$10\overline{)6030}$, where the most common error was 63, probably via 'How many tens in sixty? How many tens in thirty?' Algorithms are often used without understanding.

Write 'forty thousand and seventy' as a number.

$23 \div 1000$

The percentages of correct answers from my UK sample for three of these items were the following:

103 − 96	10 y: 64%	13 y: 70%
$23 \div 1000$	13 y: 31%	15 y: 47%
10)6030	13 y: 49%	15 y: 62%

These could be better.

I was never sure about kids being told that zero was a place holder. I thought that was when you put a bag on the seat you wanted to keep for a friend or in queues when someone asks you to 'Keep my place'.

Just occasionally, pupils get lucky when doing maths problems and achieve the 'two wrongs make a right' outcome. This was from a 14-year-old student:

$$^3\cancel{4} \; 0 \; ^1 1$$
$$- \; 3 \; 9 \; 2$$
$$0 \; 0 \; 9$$

In Chapter 10, on inconsistencies, I talk about the teen numbers and their 'reversed' names. For example, thirteen is 13 in symbols, an example of an early learning experience that might lead to later confusion, especially when dual-tasking. For example,

$$\overset{3}{}$$
$$317$$
$$+156$$
$$491$$

It is always worth looking back at early learning experiences. That could be where the intervention needs to begin, rather than at the immediate manifestation of difficulties.

Place value is a good example of using materials and visual images in a developmental way. You could look at this as using scaffolding and removing it as the learner moves through Bruner's stages of learning. Figures 5.1 to 5.8 illustrate this. Figures 5.9 to 5.11 illustrate re-naming (with one less scaffolding step). Figure 5.12 illustrates dividing by powers of 10. Note that the decimal point is *not* the centre of symmetry. If it were, then there would have to be 'oneths'. The centre of place value symmetry is the ones.

*thousands   hundreds   tens   **ones**   .   tenths   hundredths   thousandths*

I am not a fan of 'move the decimal point' as a way of dividing or multiplying by powers of 10. That is not a conceptual procedure. It could explain why the data for this (5.67 km) item from my 15-minute standardised test – converting from one metric unit to another, an objective for 11-year-old pupils in England's National Numeracy Strategy – was not impressive.

5.67 km = _____ **m   Percentage correct:**   13 y: 37%   15 y: 51%.

Place value knowledge helps with subtraction (and much more, of course), but the choice of vocabulary may not help. I offered to do some continuing professional development at my granddaughter's primary school. (Was that arrogant?) I asked the teachers what word they used for 'renaming' in subtraction. I got four different answers. That must have been confusing for pupils whenever they changed teachers. This is an issue of consistency across classes.

Basic facts

This is probably my top 'learning from the outliers' topic. Problems with learning and retaining these facts in long-term memory are among the characteristics used to define dyscalculia and maths learning difficulties but are by no means exclusive to that population.

Here is some data from the UK in 2019: The National Association of Head Teachers union surveyed members who had taken part in the government's Multiplication Tables Check (MTC) pilot in the summer term. The MTC failed to tell 94% of school leaders anything new about the ability of their Year 4 children. It just took up time and money and created stress. I liked the headline in the *Sunday Times* of 8 Sept. 2019: 'Times tables test = stress × waste of time and money'.

Another of the questions I have been asking teachers at my sessions is 'About how many of your pupils, aged 10 years, don't know all of their times table facts?' (Not very scientific but, again, big data.) The modal answer is 70%. That's far beyond any special needs population.

Back to my learning journey. (Why are we all on journeys these days?) As I said previously, multiplication facts were my first experience of abject failure when I moved from teaching in mainstream to teaching students with dyslexia. I think my employer thought a successful mainstream teacher could teach maths to students with dyslexia since he thought that dyslexia was a problem with language and not with maths. Back then, there was not much awareness of maths learning difficulties as a different specific learning difficulty that often co-occurred with dyslexia. Well, apart from Anne Henderson, Professor Mahesh Sharma and Professor Tim Miles and his wife, Elaine, no one knew much.

Addition and subtraction facts

Finger counting is a reasonably reliable, if not efficient, way of dealing with these facts, but note (later) my experience with the pupil who couldn't count back for subtraction. 'Reasonably reliable' can be a safe and reassuring place to be. Counting back is a challenging skill for some pupils and it has consequences. In 1976, Russian psychologist V. A. Krutetskii, in his book *The Psychology of Mathematical Abilities in School Children*, cited 'an ability to reverse a mental process' as one of nine characteristics that make for mathematical success.

However, counting in ones is not a process that is going to contribute to developing mathematical skills. An Australian teacher at one of my training sessions in Switzerland had lost a finger in an accident. He told me that he would show his pupils the relevant hand and tell them, 'In Australia, if you count on your fingers, they cut one off'. It's good to check the gullibility of your pupils once in a while. And their beliefs about Australia.

I return to 1, 2, 5, 10 and the visual patterns I use for five and ten. Once again, I go back to 'Use what they know to access what they don't know'. That is to treat these key facts as the building blocks for the other facts. I also think that some collections of facts are more equal than others. For addition and subtraction facts, these would be the number bonds for ten (casting out tens is a useful strategy when adding columns of numbers) and the doubles. It may also be worth refreshing pupils' memories on the commutative property.

The idea of using what you know to work out what you don't know is under-utilised in early maths, largely because of the erroneous assumption that learners *should* know this stuff by rote.

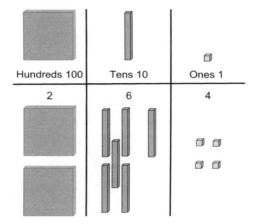

Figure 5.1 264 modelled with place value columns, supported by base-ten blocks and showing 264 as 2 hundred blocks, 6 ten blocks and 4 ones cubes.

Hundreds 100	Tens10	Ones 1
2	6	4

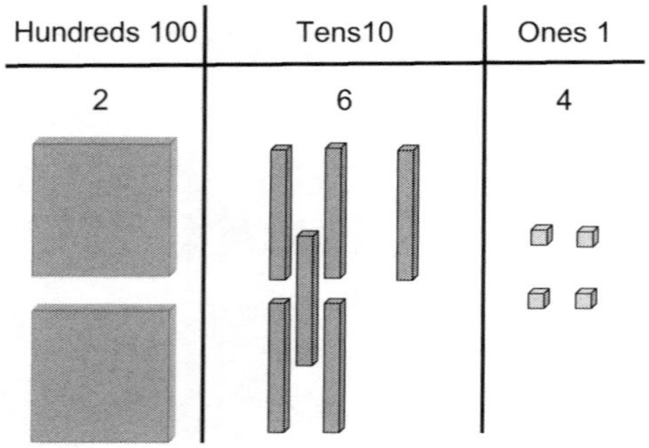

Figure 5.2 264 modelled with place value columns and showing 264 as 2 hundred blocks, 6 ten blocks and 4 ones cubes.

Hundreds 100	Tens 10	Ones 1
2	6	4

Figure 5.3 264 shown with place value columns showing 264 as 2 hundreds, 6 tens and 4 ones.

Figure 5.4 264 shown with digits.

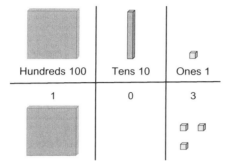

Hundreds 100	Tens 10	Ones 1
1	0	3

Figure 5.5 103 modelled with place value columns, supported by base-ten blocks and showing 103 as 1 hundred block, 0 ten blocks and 3 ones cubes.

Hundreds 100	Tens 10	Ones 1
1	0	3

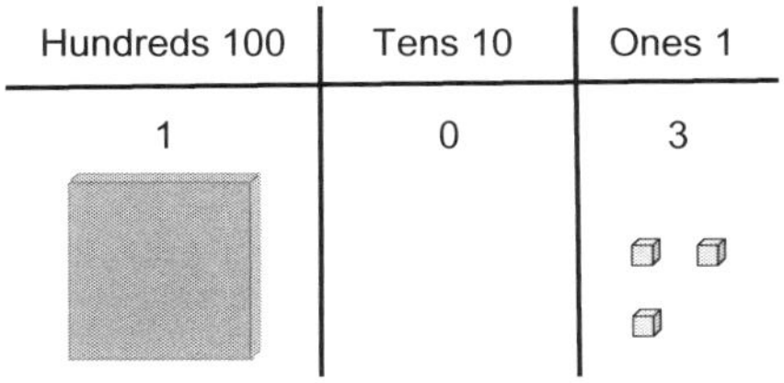

Figure 5.6 103 modelled with place value columns and showing 103 as 1 hundred block, 0 ten blocks and 3 ones cubes.

Hundreds 100	Tens 10	Ones 1
1	0	3

Figure 5.7 103 shown with place value columns, showing 103 as 1 hundred, 0 tens and 3 ones.

    1   0   3

Figure 5.8 103 shown with digits.

Interventions that address misconceptions and factual errors must be powerful enough to inhibit 'erroneous first learning'. Consistent visual images, linked to the pertinent symbols, are one way of doing this.

Multiplication and division facts

I checked Pinterest today (4 Nov. 2019) because it flagged up '40+ songs for learning times table facts'. That's almost as many songs as there are facts. Some great tunes, but the words remain problematic. Overall, Pinterest had 230 Pins on multiplication facts.

Here is some perspective on the problems with learning these facts. If you ignore the UK Government's obsession with the 12× table, then the multiplication facts that create the most problems are the 16 highlighted in the table square in Table 5.1.

Table 5.1 The times table square for facts up to 10 × 10

x	0	1	2	3	4	5	6	7	8	9	10
0	0	0	0	0	0	0	0	0	0	0	0
1	0	1	2	3	4	5	6	7	8	9	10
2	0	2	4	6	8	10	12	14	16	18	20
3	0	3	6	9	12	15	18	21	24	27	30
4	0	4	8	12	16	20	24	28	32	36	40
5	0	5	10	15	20	25	30	35	40	45	50
6	0	6	12	18	24	30	36	42	48	54	60
7	0	7	14	21	28	35	42	49	56	63	70
8	0	8	16	24	32	40	48	56	64	72	80
9	0	9	18	27	36	45	54	63	72	81	90
10	0	10	20	30	40	50	60	70	80	90	100

We should compare these 16 facts to the typical vocabulary of 10,000 words for a child who is 5 years old.

I liked the perspective from one of my former students who, despite his difficulties with times table facts, went on to gain a maths degree. He told me, 'They don't ask you what 8×7 is in the third year of a maths degree'.

Strategies for the troublesome 16

These 16 facts are very much an example for National Research Council Key Finding 2, using what you know to work out what you don't know. They are also a great opportunity for extending this to 'What else are you teaching?' I have outlined some examples below. (The methods I use are demonstrated in detail in the video tutorials on my website, mathsexplained.co.uk.) They are based on using those facts that pupils are most likely to know: $1\times$, $2\times$, $5\times$ and $10\times$.

See also Chapter 4.

For example, the $6\times$ and $7\times$ facts can be treated as partial products using those 'core' 1, 2 and 5 facts:

$$6 \times 8 = 5 \times 8 + 1 \times 8 = 40 + 8 = 48$$

$$7 \times 8 = 5 \times 8 + 2 \times 8 = 40 + 16 = 56$$

These facts and strategies can be shown with Cuisenaire rods. The vocabulary can help, too. For example, if the learner knows that 'lots of' can mean multiplication, then

6 lots of $8 = 5$ lots of $8 + 1$ lot of 8.

This strategy can be used to set the foundations for long multiplication. It also links to multiplication to repeated addition (lots of) of the same number:

$$7 \times 8 = \boxed{8 + 8 + 8 + 8 + 8} + \boxed{8 + 8} = 5 \times 8 = 2 \times 8$$

$9\times$ facts can be treated as an estimation ($10\times$) followed by a refinement of that estimation. That is based on the link of $9 = 10 - 1$ and 'Nine lots of six equals ten lots of six minus one lot of 6'. Two examples:

$$9 \times 6 = 10 \times 6 - 1 \times 6 = 60 - 6 = 54$$

$$9 \times 9 = 10 \times 9 - 1 \times 9 = 90 - 9 = 81$$

There is a check for accuracy here. The digits in the answers must add up to 9.

$$5 + 4 = 9$$

$$8 + 1 = 9$$

This works for any number $\times$ 9. For example, $9 \times 678 = 6102$. $6 + 1 + 2 = 9$

There is a method where you use fingers. See Figure 5.9. For 4×9, put down the fourth finger.

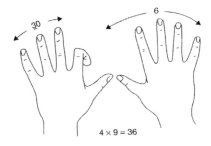

Figure 5.9 The 9× facts and fingers.

The fingers each side of the 'put down' finger are the digits that make up the answer.

The method is not secure for some learners: the ones who cannot hold down that key finger while they count the other fingers. Once again, nothing works for everyone. This method is not extending cognitive skills, so it's not at the top of my list of methods. It's an example of a quick fix and not of developing maths concepts.

For 8× facts. The only 8× fact left is 8 × 8. The strategy is repeated multiplication by 2.

$$8 \times 8 = 8 \times 2 \times 2 \times 2 = 16 \times 2 \times 2 = 32 \times 2 = 64$$

That's three reasonably straightforward sequential multiplications.

Discussion around this fact, under the 'What else are you teaching? theme, could include powers: $8 = 2 \times 2 \times 2 = 2^3 = 2^2 \times 2$. (Where is that ^{1} in 2? Should it be 2^1? Of course not, although it is correct. Surplus to requirements.)

'What else are you teaching?' is yet again a bonus here. There are partial products, estimation and appraisal, and adjustment of an estimate, repeated multiplication and powers.

Unlike this 'trick' for some 6× facts:

"Sixes Rule" for multiplying 6 by an even number:
If you multiply 6 by an even number (say, 4), it will end in the same digit, 4.
So we have 6 × 4 = __ 4.
Then the number in the tens place will be half the number in the ones place. Half of 4 is 2, so 6 × 4 = 24.

It's not a quick trick but it does work for more than one fact. I am, as ever, cautious about any method that is complicated and not developmental, but I am aware of the inverse statement to 'Nothing works for everyone'. 'Some things work for someone'.

There are quite a few tricks on the web for times table facts but rarely with a 'What else are you teaching?' bonus.

Self-voice echo

Not long after the student banged his head on the wall (Chapter 4), I was telling my old friend Dr Colin Lane about the trigger for this behaviour. The consequence was that we carried out (my first ever) classroom study using five different strategies for rote learning times tables. Our hope rested on Colin's recent research on the use of self-voice echo, where we asked students to repeat those 16 difficult times table facts, for five minutes for five days, using their own voice. This technique created the best, and longest-lasting, results compared with using other voices. Hearing the facts in my voice didn't create that much success. Teacher warning, there. Three of the five self-voice students mastered all 16 facts, long term. The downside was that one did not learn any new facts. My lesson from this? For my first (but not the last) time, I learned that 'Nothing works for everyone'. Important lesson. We published the results in the US in 1986.

I always watch the adults or children I'm assessing/diagnosing when I'm using the basic fact tests from *More Trouble with Maths* and other tests too. Many of them sub-vocalise. It's a good strategy.

Exams and times table facts

Here's another good strategy. If the student is allowed access to squared paper in the exam, it may be worth their setting up the times table (Table 5.2) with just the core facts filled in. This should not take too long. Then any other fact that crops up in the exam can be sourced from the table. For example, 7×7 from 2×7 (**14**) plus 5×7 (**35**) gives $7 \times 7 = 14 + 35 = \textbf{49}$.

Table 5.2 The key facts times table square

×	0	1	2	3	4	5	6	7	8	9	10
0	0	0	0	0	0	0	0	0	0	0	0
1	0	1	2	3	4	5	6	7	8	9	10
2	0	2	4	6	8	10	12	14	16	18	20
3	0	3	6			15					30
4	0	4	8			20					40
5	0	5	10	15	20	25	30	35	40	45	50
6	0	6	12			30					60
7	0	7	14			35		49			70
8	0	8	16			40					80
9	0	9	18			45					90
10	0	10	20	30	40	50	60	70	80	90	100

Final note on times tables

My experience and the data for standardising the basic fact tests in *More Trouble with Maths* tell me that $6 \times 7 = 42$ is the least well-known multiplication fact. I'm sure it's a coincidence, but for those of you who remember the hugely popular *Hitchhiker's Guide to the Galaxy* by Douglas Adams, the 'Answer to the Ultimate Question of Life, the Universe, and Everything' was 42. Apparently, this was calculated by an enormous supercomputer named 'Deep Thought' over a period of 7.5 million years. Unfortunately, no one knows what the question is. I have tried to apply this to my maths teaching. So we know an answer, but we don't know what the question is. I'm not there yet.

Division

There are more links here. Division links to repeated subtraction. Division is the inverse operation to multiplication. Also, using links gives an opportunity to review those previous topics that have relevance to the current topic. They should also lead to flexible ways of carrying out division rather than the somewhat complicated and dubious standard algorithm that we use in England. The method doesn't do much to help the concept of place value.

That standard method makes another demand of learners, the ability to organise work on a page. This may make a further case for giving some students squared paper. There may need to be some check about what size of square suits an individual learner.

When I was collecting the data for standardising my tests of basic facts, I couldn't help but notice this paper for the basic division facts:

gave up
I can't sink
strate
Name I always ansirs
get 2 asirs
$2 \div 1 = 2$ $4 \div 1 = 4$ age 12 y 6 m $4 \div 2 = 1$

M/F M date

$6 \div 2 = 1$ $6 \div 3 =$ $9 \div 3 =$

I thought his response was quite measured and tolerant. It also showed that he took the blame for the problem. Erroneously.

I found from the data that division facts for 1 were not well answered by many students. Maybe teachers don't give enough exposure to them. Multiplying by 1 crops up in equivalent fractions, so we need to be careful not to say 'Multiplying by 1 doesn't change the number'. Instead, 'Multiplying by 1 doesn't change the value of a number'. That deals with examples like $2/3 = 10/15$. The numbers may have been changed by multiplying by $5/5$, but the fraction remains the same value.

Language and the interlinking of operations might help with basic division facts, so instead of asking 'What is 36 divided by 9?', ask 'What do I multiply 9 by to get 36?' or 'How many 9s can I take away from 36?' It might help some students if this is demonstrated with Cuisenaire rods. Chunking into core facts can be a big help again; $5 \times 9 = 45$ could be a first attempt and as an estimate.

Long(ish) division

That last question, 'How many can I take away?', is the basis of the standard algorithm for long division, although that is not always the way it is explained. For example, 'How many threes are there in 72?' goes something like this:

$3\overline{)7\ 2}$ 'How many threes in 7?' (Actually it's 70, but it's an algorithm … Tricky for the literal/inchworm pupil because 7 doesn't turn up in the 3x table, but say he gets to '2').

$\frac{2}{3\overline{)7\ 2}}$ 'There are two 3s and 1 left over'. Note that '1' is not 'one 3'. That 1 is one ten. We write it next to the 2, so that 2 becomes 12.

$\frac{2}{3\overline{)7^12}}$ So 2 becomes 12 and we ask, 'How many threes in 12?' The answer is 4, so we've finished.

$\frac{2\ 4}{3\overline{)7^12}}$ This is sometimes called the 'bus stop' method. You know the legend; you wait ages for a bus/method to come along and then three come together. Confusing but maybe 3 are enough.

A modification, fitting more with the philosophy of this book, could be,

'How many 3s can I subtract from 72?'

Try writing a few multiples/partial products: $2 \times 3 = 6$ $5 \times 3 = 15$ $10 \times 3 = 30$ $20 \times 3 = 60$. That also gives a basis for an estimation.

Then set up repeated subtractions of partial products.

```
  72
- 60    20   x   3
  12
-  6     2   x   3          24 lots of 3 were subtracted. Answer 24.
   6
-  6     2   x   3
   0
```

(The pupil may recognise $4 \times 3 = 12$ and reduce the number of steps.)

The procedure can be used for more complex divisions, again using key number multiples (for example, $6001 \div 17$).

Set up key multiples/partial products:

$2 \times 17 = 34$	$20 \times 17 = 340$	$200 \times 17 = 3400$
$5 \times 17 = 85$	$50 \times 17 = 850$	$500 \times 17 = 8500$
$10 \times 17 = 170$	$100 \times 17 = 1700$	

(The patterns $2\times$ and $20\times$, $5\times$ and $50\times$, $10\times$ and $100\times$ refresh place value knowledge.)

Make an estimate:

6001 lies between 3400 and 8500, about half-way between 200×17 and 500×17, so estimate around 350.

The key partial products provide the information for the estimate.

Do the subtractions:

```
  6001
 −3400    200x
  2601
 −1700    100x
   901
  −850     50x          200 + 100 + 50 + 2 + 1 = 353
    51
   −34      2x
    17               Check back with the pre-calculation estimate.
    17      1x
```

There is more logic and more developmental maths in this modification to the traditional algorithm. There may be a few more steps, not always, but they use the easier multiples, rather than intermediate steps that ask questions such as 'How many 17s in 90?'. The layout is more straightforward. As ever, remember that nothing works for everyone.

And there is that built-in estimation.

There is more on division, with visual images to support learning, in the Maths Explained tutorials.

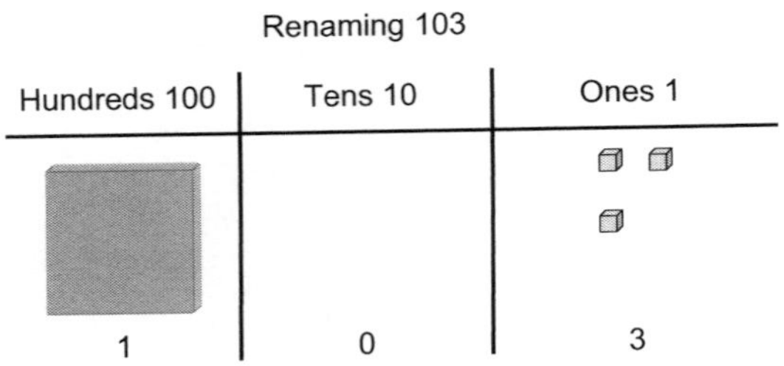

Renaming 103

Hundreds 100	Tens 10	Ones 1
		□ □
		□
1	0	3

Figure 5.10 103 modelled with place value columns, supported by base-ten blocks and showing 103 as 1 hundred block and 3 ones cubes.

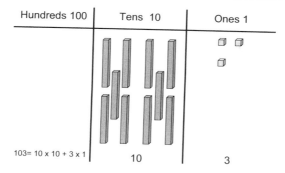

Figure 5.11 103 renamed with base-ten blocks showing 10 ten blocks and 3 ones cubes.

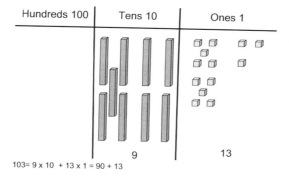

Figure 5.12 103 renamed with base-ten blocks showing 9 ten blocks and 13 ones cubes.

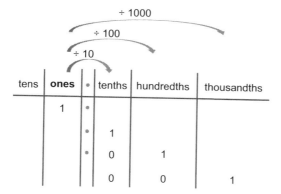

Figure 5.13 Place value columns used to show 1 divided by powers of 10.

Figure 5.14 'What you know'. $5 + 5 = 10$.

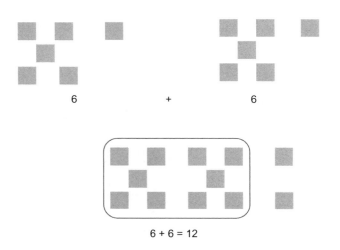

$6 + 6 = 12$

Figure 5.15 Using $5 + 5 = 10$ and $5 + 1 = 6$ to show the 'double' fact $6 + 6$.

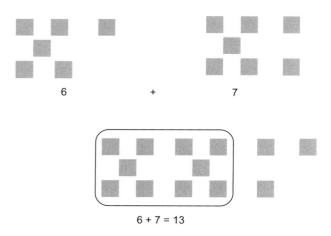

$6 + 7 = 13$

Figure 5.16 Using the 'doubles' fact $6 + 6$ to access $6 + 7$ (doubles + 1) = 13.

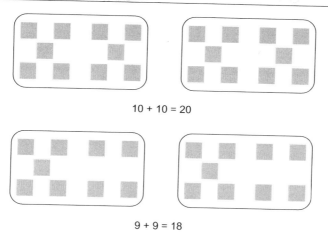

10 + 10 = 20

9 + 9 = 18

Figure 5.17 Using the 'doubles' fact 10 + 10 to access 9 + 9 as (10 − 1 + 10 − 1) = 18.

Chapter 6

Learner characteristics and key skills

Again, I'll start with the outliers, in this case the ones in the bottom 5% of achievers, the students with dyscalculia. Defining dyscalculia is a challenge. A key contributing factor in defining maths learning problems is that they are about humans and humans are difficult to define in comparison with, say, the momentum of an object (mass times velocity).

Working on the hypothesis that there is a spectrum of difficulties in maths, the only definition we are going to find is at the extreme end, dyscalculia. However, experience and the spectrum tell me that the identified difficulties will not be confined to this group, but it is a good place to start.

Learning difficulties, even if not classified as severe, can dominate the impression a school has of a student, such that the school sees the problem and not the student. Seeing past and addressing the problems that create learning issues reveal the person. It is never just about a 'label'. Well, that label might be important in the early stages as the pupil's problems are diagnosed, but it must not define expected progress and achievement and certainly not the individual.

It seems to me that mainstream is far less likely to consider and utilise the learning characteristics of pupils than it is to consider new teaching pedagogies, such as Shanghai maths. All pupils will have a heterogeneous mix of learning characteristics and each of these (often interacting) characteristics or factors is on a continuum. Consequently, it will be ineffective to teach just to the 'norm', whatever that is. So the question is, is it possible to teach to a wider range of learners? Can we teach in a way that minimises the number of learners who are disconnected from learning? And will the lessons we learn from the outliers help us to do that? You might have guessed that I think the answer to both of these questions is 'yes'.

The benefit here is that we are in with a chance of improving outcomes for all our students whilst reducing the number who have, or develop, maths learning difficulties and maths refusal.

We should keep in mind that maths requires a constellation of abilities, not just the ability to rote learn stuff.

There is an impressive body of research on the factors that can influence maths learning. Examples are working memory (start with looking at Alan Baddeley's pioneering work) and maths anxiety (check out the Maths Anxiety Trust). Much of this research comes from studies into maths learning difficulties and many of these factors interact. For example, anxiety can have a negative impact on working memory. (The pioneer here is Mark Ashcraft.) This makes individuals even more individual.

Now, that could lead us to believe that it is all too complicated to deal with in a busy classroom and thus acts as a barrier to implementing changes, but we do not have to introduce all our new approaches and new attitudes at one time. And we should constantly review what we do introduce. Teamwork, such as department meetings or informal and regular chats with other teachers, learning support assistants and lecturers, can be hugely beneficial here.

As ever, any teaching should be designed, as far as possible, to pre-empt 'wrong' learning. That goal will be heavily dependent on being aware of and responding to learner characteristics.

Key factors

I have listed the main factors that influence learning, and thus can contribute to difficulties in maths, in Table 6.1. I'll say a little about each factor. Figure 6.1 shows some of the interactions between the factors. That complicates the situation and makes it even more important to be aware of the influences on learning. I have also included Figure 6.2 showing the normal distribution to remind the reader that, in addition to interactions with other factors, each factor will lie somewhere on that normal distribution. Any innovation and any intervention must actively acknowledge these factors.

A sense of proportion: Note that 68.26% lie within 1 standard deviation (SD) each side of the mean and that 15.86% lie below (and above) this.

Table 6.1 Factors that influence learning

An ability to work with symbols
Maths vocabulary
Short-term memory
Working memory
Long-term maths memory
Speed of processing mathematical tasks
Cognitive style
An ability to sequence (forwards and backwards)
An ability to generalise and see patterns (to classify)
Anxiety, fear and risk avoidance

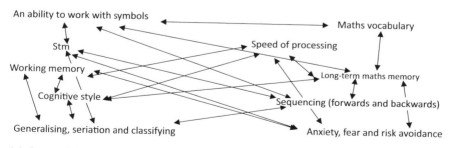

Figure 6.1 Some of the interactions between the key learning factors.

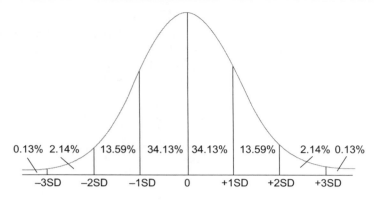

Figure 6.2 The normal distribution.

An ability to work with symbols

There are ten digit symbols for number: 0, 1, 2, 3, 4, 5, 6, 7, 8 and 9. How they are combined to make numbers depends on place value, which means that the value a digit represents in a number depends on its place in the sequence of digits that make up the number.

Consistency is reassuring when a pupil is learning new knowledge. It is easy to underestimate or overlook the inconsistencies of early maths. For example, with the early skill of counting, after nine, 9, numbers are represented by two digits as in ten, 10. When my son told me that my grandson could count to ten, I was very proud and resisted the temptation to add to my praise, 'Ah, but does he understand the significance of the 0 and its place in 10?'

Unfortunately for insecure learners, the vocabulary for the first two-digit numbers is inconsistent in the English language (not so in Cantonese or Welsh). Eleven and twelve are one-offs, and the teen number names are backwards compared with their digits. For example, we say 'sixteen' and write '16'. It could be good to show all the numbers for, say, 20 to 60 first and then focus back on 11 to 19 as exceptions.

And in French there are some interesting examples of words for number. For example, 92 is said as 'four twenties and twelve'.

The symbols for the operations are sometimes hidden or partially hidden.

Fractions hide a division symbol; for example, $\frac{4}{5}$ means $4 \div 5$.

Symbols don't always appear to act consistently. For example, with $\frac{4}{5} \times \frac{3}{7}$, the × symbol works to multiply 4×3 and 5×7 and gives $\frac{12}{35}$, but with $\frac{4}{5} + \frac{3}{7}$, the + symbol is not applied to both the numerators and the denominators, so $\frac{7}{12}$ is an incorrect, and frequently occurring, answer.

Algebra has its symbol problems, too. For example, there is no multiplication symbol for ab or a(b+c).

For pupils who have problems with the order of symbols, 2a and a^2 may be confusing.

We happily accept that 0 means zero, nothing. The Romans didn't have a symbol for 'nothing' as they thought it was illogical to do so. But 0 is vital in place value in the Hindu–Arabic number system. Its presence in a number can cause confusion, especially when an algorithm is involved (for example, in subtractions such as

$$
\begin{array}{r}
1000 \\
- \ 495 \\
\hline
\end{array}
$$

or when writing a number in digits such as 'fifty thousand and fifty').

Perhaps that Roman intuitive attitude to 'nothing' persists today.

The interactions between symbols and vocabulary can be challenging, too.

Maths vocabulary

Unfortunately, the potential for confusion with maths vocabulary isn't restricted to the teen numbers. Once again early maths has the potential for inconsistencies and confusion, and once again there is an argument for returning to early curriculum content, if only briefly, to address misconceptions and insecurely grasped concepts.

There is a choice of words for each of the four operation symbols and for the = symbol. Choice can be confusing. An example of resisting choice is that many children ask for one method to solve problems (for example, subtraction) and they also want that one method to apply to all similar problems.

The problem with having many words for the same operation is exacerbated by the inclusion of words that are taken from everyday life and dropped into maths, such as 'take away'. Some of the other words used are obviously maths words, such as 'multiplication' (although I seem to recall some non-mathematical use of this in my school days' religious studies lessons).

Just how the vocabulary is used can create further confusion. For example, '7 take away 3' has the digits in a helpful order for converting to 7 – 3. 'Take 3 away from 7' reverses that order. Sometimes, what appears to be a simple modification creates a disproportionate problem for learners.

Everyday interpretations can get in the way of understanding. For example, 'How many sixes in 66?' could be answered as two. Everyday vocabulary may not be helpful in a maths lesson unless you remember to explain that you are using it to 'talk' maths.

I'm a believer that materials, manipulatives and visual images can be used to reduce the potential for confusion and help make the first learning experience a correct one. We need to pre-empt errors and mis-learning whenever possible.

Short-term memory

It's a great name because it describes itself. It's a memory that is held for only a brief time and then it's gone and no amount of concentration will get it back. Saying to a student, 'Concentrate, think' won't help. Teachers can compound that negative experience by saying, 'But I told you it twice'. It's still gone. In my mature (old) years, I tend to forget the names of people I've just met. That's it. No entry to my brain. Until someone comes along and calls them by name, thus giving me another chance to get their name past my short-term memory (STM) deficit.

Back in 2000, I did a study on the role of STM for sequential information in maths. The groups were both of male students who were 16 years old; 28 were boys with (severe) dyslexia from my specialist school and 27 were non-dyslexic boys matched on predicted exam grades in maths. Both groups were given a memory for sequence sub-test from the Goldman–Fristoe–Woodcock Auditory Memory tests. The results indicated a relationship between STM and maths grades achieved for the mainstream students (who scored higher on STM capacity than the students with dyslexia). This was not the case with the students with dyslexia. My optimistic hypothesis was that appropriate teaching could address some of the learning difficulties that can block maths learning. Our high GCSE (General Certificate of Secondary Education) results in maths supported that hypothesis. (We were awarded Beacon School status by the UK Government for our work on maths.)

What any communicator/teacher should be proactively aware of is that, should the instructions or information they are saying exceed the listener's STM, then ALL of it will be forgotten. That is a waste of time for the teacher and totally ineffective and frustrating for the learner. After determining which of their students have weak STM, teachers should adjust the way they communicate, such as writing notes on a display or board or allowing students to do this for themselves on a pad or wipe-clean board. Or maybe use a 'buddy'?

Working memory

This is another name that does what it says. You can read much more about working memory in Gathercole and Alloway's 2008 book *Working Memory and Learning: A Practical Guide for Teachers*. But, for this chapter, I want to give an overview of the importance of working memory in maths.

Mental arithmetic is challenging for many people. It requires a good working memory. It also helps the learner if their STM capacity is enough to remember the question. Quick access to pertinent facts is helpful, too, as this reduces the load on working memory. Not being anxious about the task also helps. Anxiety reduces working memory capacity.

There is a link here with cognitive style. A grasshopper style will take an example such as $356 - 198$ and convert it to $358 - 200$, removing the need to carry out renaming and thus reducing the demand on working memory. Carrying out the computation as $356 - 198$ by the written algorithm, but in your head, will require more steps and more working memory.

I love the title of this paper: 'Preschoolers doing arithmetic: The concepts are willing, but the working memory is weak' (Klein and Bisanz, 2000).

Long-term maths memory

I'm happy to admit to being impressed by what people know and recall in pub quiz nights and I'm even more impressed by the breadth of knowledge of the contestants on University Challenge. And their retrieval is often quick, which is even more impressive. My guess is that you could slow down pub quiz nights by asking more maths questions. Come to think of it, have you ever seen a maths quiz night advertised by a pub?

I have added 'maths' to long-term memory in the subtitle. I am a great believer in Howard Gardner's theory of multiple intelligences. I think that, in addition to applying to intelligences, 'multiple' applies to long-term memories. Not everyone has all of Gardner's eight intelligences at the same level. My experience is that not everyone has the same capacity of long-term memory for every topic, partly down to the brain and partly down to motivation and interests. It's one of the reasons why, in life, we get specialists.

It's worth noting that school is a bad place to be if you have weak long-term memories for spelling and for basic facts and procedures in maths. Rote learning is often the dominant pedagogy for these topics.

Some people find that getting maths information securely into long-term memory is a natural and powerful skill. Some don't. The normal distribution will apply here, too. Unfortunately, despite the evidence, despite the reality, there is a strong belief in enough (well, maybe too many) curriculum and policy makers that all children can rote learn the times table facts. And retrieve them quickly. That belief is applied to much of the rest of maths that children must do in schools. Who was it who said, 'Practice makes perfect'? If only it were that simple. But many people say it and maybe even believe it. As with a lot of clichéd sayings, it's more complicated than that.

When pupils fail to memorise or the process is too complex, we sometimes use mnemonics. One of the problems with mnemonics is that you usually need to remember more to recall less. This limits its effectiveness. For example, one of the most famous maths mnemonics is for $8 \times 8 = 64$, 'I ate and I ate 'til I was sick on the floor'. And I guess we all know that to divide a fraction by a fraction 'You turn upside down and multiply'. My visual image for that is slightly off-task and involves gymnastics. Does make it memorable, though. Might not help understanding.

Sometimes, pertinent information and ideas from an old piece of research crop up many years later in a slightly different style. When I worked in the US in the mid-80s, I found a monologue on arithmetic (Buswell and Judd) from 1925 which highlighted the powerful and lasting influence of the first learning experience of new information. They observed that, whether this learning is incorrect or correct, it will be a dominant entry to the brain and that subsequent attempts to rectify incorrect learning will be only temporary. I think this describes the reason why some people might answer 54, a close answer from the times table square, when asked the answer to 7×8. Once 54 is established, it's hard to remove it.

A version of this observation on human behaviour came from Luchins in 1942. I love the name used for this, *Einstellung*. It refers to a person's predisposition to solve a given problem in a specific way even though better or more appropriate methods for solving the problem exist. The *Einstellung* effect is the negative effect of previous experience when trying to solve new problems. It is about the dangers of the habit mastering the individual rather than the individual mastering the habit.

Key Finding 1 from the National Research Council (NRC) book *How People Learn* (2000) draws the same conclusion about the power and perseverance of the first learning experience.

Then I came across this quote, from Tolstoy (1828–1910):

The most difficult subjects can be explained to the most slow-witted man if he has not formed any idea of them already, but the simplest thing cannot be made clear to the most intelligent man if he is firmly persuaded that he knows already, without a shadow of a doubt, what is laid before him.

Useful stuff like Tolstoy's quote can lie dormant for a long time. Unfortunately, sometimes useless stuff can flourish immediately.

So we need to try to get that first learning to be correct. Casual teaching, rushed teaching, uncertain teaching that does not secure the knowledge is detrimental to any of the future learning that depends on that information. If we do try to replace the 'wrong' learning, then we need to create a very powerful input to the brain. This certainly eliminates any 'more of the same' input. The problem of inhibition (of wrong stuff) has recently been highlighted by Denes Szucs and his team (2013) and David Geary (2015).

Maybe this concept is linked to mindset?

There is some mileage in being efficient in selecting what you commit to long-term memory, especially when you consider that second NRC Key Finding (Chapter 1) about using what you know to work out what you don't know. I strongly believe that linking facts and knowledge strengthens understanding and that what you link and understand you are more likely to remember. Prioritise the stuff that's most useful, both for its own worth and for where it can lead.

Finally, I should mention precision teaching and mastery. I dabbled with precision teaching of basic facts back in the 1980s with the help of a very cooperative and patient 13-year-old student. I based my intervention on a hierarchical list of 23 steps for whole number addition. The list came from an American book, *Guiding Each Child's Learning of Mathematics: A Diagnostic Approach to Instruction*. What a great title! The book was written by four of my heroes, one of whom is a superhero, Robert Ashlock, author of *Error Patterns in Computation,* which reached 10 editions. I persuaded Ashlock to come out of retirement and write a chapter in my edited book, *The Routledge International Handbook of Dyscalculia and Mathematical Learning Difficulties* (2015). Back to the student. He worked very patiently with me for 5 to 10 minutes a day as we worked down (or up?) the 23 steps, starting with 'sums to 10' and ending with 'regrouping thousands'. The trouble was, when we got to step 23, he'd forgotten most of the preceding steps. And the time we spent getting to number 23 was not going to be in any way effective for catch-up. I abandoned that version of precision teaching.

'Mastery' has been a buzzword lately. Sometimes, 'new' ideas attract more attention than they deserve. Not because they are poor ideas but because they can push equally good, or even better, ideas into the background. It's that awareness that 'Nothing works for everyone' we should keep in mind. But new ideas can generate optimism. I found it an interesting comment, linked to mastery, that we in the UK admire maths education in Singapore (and other Asian countries). I do, too, and have done 5 days of consultation for their Ministry of Education on maths learning difficulties and special needs in maths. I love the *Singapore Model Method for Learning Mathematics* (2009) by Kho Tek Hong et al. (see Chapter 9). What really impresses me is that their framework acknowledges the 1982 UK Cockcroft Report's influence on the teaching of maths in schools. Such a shame we didn't act on it as they did in Singapore.

It seems that mastery has not produced the gains the Government and the National Centre for Excellence in the Teaching of Mathematics (NCETM) had anticipated (Boylan, M.: 'Remastering mathematics: Mastery, remixes and mash-ups', MT 266, April 2019, 14–18). By the way, is it dangerous from an expectation perspective sticking that E into NCETM? It's not there in the US equivalent, the National Council of Teachers of Mathematics.

Chapter 4 on 'Developmental maths' is very much about linking procedures around multiplication in a developmental way. Unsurprisingly, so is Chapter 8 on 'Linking', where there is a broader overview of this principle.

Speed of processing

This is another example of the beliefs and culture that influence maths education. For example, for whatever reason, the belief is that children in the UK who will take the national times table tests will have to answer each item in a maximum of 6 seconds.

The most frequently awarded accommodation for taking exams for students who have learning difficulties is for them to be given more time for an exam. So the problem, the existence of slow processing, is acknowledged. But some may ask, why a time limit for exams anyway? For any student? The normal distribution is likely to apply here, too.

Pressurising students to work to tight time restraints can create anxiety. This impacts on working memory capacity and may also trigger withdrawal from the task.

So maybe teachers should look at the homework and the tasks that they give to their students and ask themselves, 'Do I need to set all of these questions? Which ones are useful for consolidating learning? Which ones are superfluous? Do I give the same to all my class? (Differentiation). Could some result in incorrect learning? Is this just "busy work"'?

In an informal survey I did in 2001 and later presented at an international conference, I asked students with dyslexia what they found helpful and what they found unhelpful in the classroom. One of the main answers in regard to the latter was 'Teachers who go too fast and expect too much'. I'll talk about expectations later.

Sequencing (forwards and backwards)

Sequencing can be about the very basics of maths, such as counting and place value. It can be about the sequence of steps to solve a problem.

Counting backwards is difficult for some students, especially if it's slightly away from the usual, such as counting back in odd numbers. With young children, we tend to practise counting forwards far more often than we ask them to count backwards.

We expect students to be able to reverse procedures, too. That's quite common in algebra. Sometimes, we use BOMDAS (brackets order multiplication division addition subtraction) or BODMAS (brackets order division multiplication addition subtraction) to support the use of a sequence of steps in algebra, or we use FOIL (first outer inner last) to work out brackets. People do not make up acronyms in maths unless there is a perceived need.

Once again, I will mention early research (see also Chapter 5), this time from a book from Russian psychologist Krutetskii, *The Psychology of Mathematical Abilities in Schoolchildren* (1968, translated into English in 1976; languages are not one of my multiple intelligences), about the characteristic skills needed to be good at maths. One of the seven characteristics is 'Being able to switch from a direct to a reverse train of thought'.

Working memory capacity can be a factor here, especially for mental arithmetic.

Cognitive style

Metacognition has become a regular part of maths vocabulary of late. Once again, I return to *How People Learn*, where Key Finding 3 is about the importance of metacognition. I think that one of the most useful and revealing questions that a teacher can ask a student is 'Can you tell me/explain to me how you worked that out?' It is an example of a diagnostic approach to teaching.

Back in 1986, along with colleagues John Bath and Dwight Knox, we published *The Test of Cognitive Style in Mathematics* in the US. A version of this is part of the test protocol in my book on diagnosis, *More Trouble with Maths* (3rd edition, 2020).

The interaction of cognitive style with other factors, such as working memory, illuminates different profiles of maths learning difficulties. Chapter 7 explains the implications in more detail. I consider the implications to be highly significant for teaching and learning maths.

Generalising, seriation and classifying

This is another 'then and now' topic.

Then: Piaget and Szeminska (1941) suggested a relationship between 'seriation' (or the logical ability to sort objects on the basis of differences while ignoring similarities) and 'classification' (or the logical ability to sort objects on the basis of similarities while ignoring differences) and the understanding of number.

Now: Desoete (2015) noted that 'Seriation and classification (as logical thinking skills) and procedural and conceptual counting knowledge are significant predictive indicators for mathematical learning disabilities in kindergarten'.

These skills support long-term memory. They support understanding and logic and problem solving. It would be wrong to assume that they do not need overt nurturing and developing in a classroom. We cannot rely on pupils just absorbing and integrating these skills into their learning.

Anxiety, fear and risk avoidance

I have dedicated Chapter 13 to these vital topics.

Chapter 7

Metacognition

Here are two pertinent quotes to start the chapter. The first one, from the National Research Council (US), you've seen before:

> A 'metacognitive' approach to instruction can help students learn to take control of their own learning by defining learning goals and monitoring their progress in achieving them.

And the second is from Singapore:

> Metacognition is one of the five pillars of successful learning in mathematics.

I like that Key Finding quote. I do revere the book it came from and I like the prominence it gives to metacognition. There are only three Key Findings in the book, so metacognition is rated highly. I think 'taking control of your own learning' can be a challenge, but it is a laudable goal, even when only partially achieved.

Work I did back in the 1980s with two American colleagues looked at how students solved maths problems (and how teachers taught this skill). Our data collection strategy was based around the question 'Can you tell me how you worked that out?' We had to find maths problems that could be solved by more than one method and that generated methods which were close to being equally attractive to students who had different cognitive styles. That was the hypothesis, students have different cognitive styles. Of course, teachers will too if the hypothesis is confirmed. As ever, there are many factors involved here, but one straightforward example that worked was the mental arithmetic question, 224 + 97. We'll return to that later.

Another quote:

> Teachers need to move from the single idea to multiple ideas, and to relate and the expand these ideas such that learners construct and reconstruct knowledge and ideas.
>
> Hattie (2009), p. 239

Some background

I'll start the background overview with the Nobel Prize–winning economist Daniel Kahneman and a quote from his book *Thinking, Fast and Slow* (2012), where he describes two styles of thinking:

System 1 operates automatically and quickly, with little or no effort and no sense of voluntary control.

System 2 allocates attention to the effortful mental activities that demand it, including complex calculations. The operations of System 2 are often associated with the subjective experience of agency, choice and concentration.

As one might expect from a Nobel Prize winner, these descriptions are just so very clever, succinct and perceptive.

Some way ahead of everyone else in maths education, back in 1971, UK mathematician and psychologist Richard Skemp wrote about 'instrumental' and 'relational thinking' in maths. The names are self-explanatory. In one sense, this hypothesis was an indirect criticism of the way maths was often taught at that time (that is, as the manipulation of symbols with little or no meaning attached and little or no understanding of the underlying concepts). The dominant reliance was on rote.

Sometimes, students collude with this instrumental approach. The night before her big national examination for maths, a colleague's daughter said to her, 'Tell me how to do these problems, Mum. Don't explain why it works. I haven't got time'.

My US colleagues Bath and Knox (1986) coined the labels 'inchworm' and 'grasshopper' to describe different cognitive styles based on their interpretation of the ways these creatures moved around. We thought that those ways of moving were illustrative of the different ways people solve maths problems, and it helped us to remember which label described which style. (There was some research from the US which used the labels 'Thinking Styles 1 and 2'. There's not much chance of relating there.)

Does it matter how you think in maths?

The quick answer is 'yes'. The longer answer will suggest some reasons why it matters.

As a teacher, I feel I am obliged to show my students how to be flexible in their thinking. That is a lot different from showing them which way to think. Fortunately, maths is a remarkably good subject for encouraging flexible thinking.

Let me take a couple of examples. One is 'everyday', the other is more classroom-based.

I had finished an enjoyable Thai meal in my hometown and was paying my bill via the card machine. Maybe it was the Asian beer, maybe I was even more relaxed than usual, but somehow I typed in my card code and my tip together and ended up with a bill for more than half a million pounds. The meal wasn't quite that good! Luckily my skill with estimation, a grasshopper skill, saved me. Or at least, I did look at and appraise the amount. I didn't feel it was necessary to do an inchworm check on the actual total. I'd saved myself a lot of money.

One of the many reasons I like the Singapore model method (Chapter 12) for problem solving is that the process makes students take time to read and interpret the problem and think before rushing in. Often, there is a culture of speed of working in a maths classroom. This does not always encourage reflective and flexible thinking.

The lesson from metacognition for teachers is that we need to be flexible and adaptable in our thinking (and teaching) and encourage and develop this behaviour in our learners. There is, as is the way with a continuum, the greatest risk at the extremes of the spectrum. A restricted, 'one-style-dominant' cognitive style will be a handicap to becoming a successful mathematician. For example, in England, a student could get every answer correct on an Advanced-level maths exam and fail if they did not document their reasoning. This grasshopper tendency coupled with a lack of documentation is discouraged and penalised by the examination boards.

The issue of 'showing your working' can start when pupils are quite young. A primary teacher showed me this example from a 7-year-old girl when asked to show how she got her answer (Figure 7.1):

$$32 - 19 = 27$$

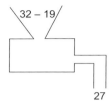

27

Figure 7.1 How to calculate 32 – 19.

Grasshoppers and Inchworms

I have found that the easiest and most effective way I can describe the behaviours of the two cognitive styles is with a table that considers the three stages of solving a problem. The table is taken from *Mathematics for Dyslexics and Dyscalculics* (4th edition) by Chinn and Ashcroft. A version originally appeared in 1986 in *The Test of Thinking Style* by Bath, Chinn and Knox (Table 7.1).

Table 7.1 Cognitive styles of the inchworm and the grasshopper

	Inchworm	Grasshopper
First approach to a problem	1. Focuses on the parts and details 2. Looks at the numbers and facts to select a suitable formula or procedure	1. Overviews, holistic, puts together 2. Looks at the numbers and facts to estimate an answer or narrow down the range of answers. Uses controlled exploration. This is more cerebral than guessing.
Solving the problem	3. Formula-procedure-oriented 4. Constrained focus. Uses one method, which hopefully works on all similar problems 5. Works in serially ordered steps, usually forward 6. Uses numbers exactly as given (numerically literal) 7. More comfortable with paper and pen. Documents method.	3. Answer-oriented 4. Flexible focus; uses a range of methods, often dependent on the numbers involved 5. Often works back from a trial answer 6. Adjusts, breaks down/builds up numbers to make the calculation easier 7. Rarely documents method; performs calculations mentally (and intuitively)
Checking and evaluating answers. (Verification).	8. Unlikely to check or evaluate answers. If a check is done, it will be by the same procedure or method. 9. Often does not understand procedures or values of numbers. Works mechanically.	8. Likely to appraise and evaluate an answer against original estimate 9. Good understanding of numbers and relationships

So let's return to 224 + 97.

A grasshopper cognitive style would round the 97 to 100, add to 224 for an interim 324 and subtract 3 (asking 'Is this answer bigger or smaller than the final answer?') to obtain 321, or maybe add 3 to 97 and subtract 3 from 224 (net change 0) to create 221 + 100. The load on working memory is much less than that required for the inchworm method, which is:

Visualise the computation as it would be written on paper,

$$224$$
$$+\underline{97}$$

And off we go with mental arithmetic, à la written arithmetic: 'Add the ones digits, 11, place 1 in the (mental) ones column, hold it there in memory, retrieve the tens digits from memory, "carry" 1 ten and add the tens digits, 12, place the 2 in the tens column, carry 1 hundred, retrieve the hundreds digit from memory, add this 2 hundred to give 3 hundred. The digits were generated in the order of 1 one, 2 tens and 3 hundreds. Reverse the digits to get 321'.

You can see why mental arithmetic, especially with an inchworm method, demands so much working memory and why teachers need to know the working memory capacity of an inchworm student before they ask an inappropriate question.

I should mention that any distractions in a classroom are likely to reduce working memory capacity even further. This is often overlooked as a contributor to difficulties.

I should also mention that anxiety about the task will reduce working memory capacity.

I used to wonder who on that curriculum designers' planet thought that starting maths lessons with mental arithmetic questions was motivational for students. I wonder about this still.

Working with audiences at my talks on cognitive style, I sense that more teachers use the 100 method these days. This is encouraging in that it suggests more teachers are taking a flexible approach to thinking about maths, at least in this one type of example.

Let's look at one more example and then we'll look at some interactions of cognitive style with other learning factors.

About the time I was working on cognitive style with Bath and Knox, I went into my local (UK) post office to buy some stamps. Back then, the assistants had to calculate cost and change without a computer doing it for them. I asked for two stamps at 17p each and two at 23p each. The assistant muttered under her breath (self-voice echo) whilst jotting down a couple of numbers, 'Two seventeens are, um, 34p. Now, two 23ps are 46p, so that's 34 plus 46. Um, 80p'. Inchworm. There was a large queue behind me, so I decided not to engage in a cognition tutorial.

My post office tutorial would have suggested re-ordering the problem to add 17 and 23 (number bonds for 10 are key facts) to get 40p followed by doubling to get 80p. An effective check would be to do an average stamp cost as $80 \div 4 = 20p$. Number bonds for 10 are especially useful facts in arithmetic.

The tutorial would have offered a general guide for problem solving, 'Think before you calculate'. I thought the advice 'Do make sure you have explored the various cognitive options before you start your calculation' might have sounded a tad pretentious, certainly to the queue behind me.

In our data collection for the items that made up our Test of Cognitive Style, we included some 'shape and space' items. We subsequently found that some students were inchworm on 'shape and space' and grasshopper on computations and some were vice versa. Some were 'terminal' inchworms on both. Many of the grasshoppers were self-taught flexible thinkers.

I am wary of over-simplification, but sometimes it can act as a succinct reflection, so here goes: Inchworms tend to want to know 'How do I do it?' whereas grasshoppers want to know 'Why do I do it like this?'

Cognitive style and teachers

Of course, there are also inchworm and grasshopper teachers. This may be one reason why some pupils say, 'I really understood the way Mrs Brown taught maths, but I can't understand Mr Green'.

Cognitive style may influence the way teachers judge work. (The implications of that would be quite scary if that comment applied to those who set examinations and write mark schemes.) When I delivered in-service training to a maths department in a prestigious school in the UK, I gave teachers answers from two students to the same question. Here's the question. Read it carefully.

Four farmers let their 32 sheep graze together on the hills for the summer. In the autumn, they sent their children to bring them down.... (Figure 7.2).

Figure 7.2 The sheep on a hill problem.

(*It came with this illustration because it's a real-life problem, although 32 sheep between four farmers may not be real-life.*)

Sandra was to bring five more than Alan.

Alan was to bring two less than Robert.

Jackie was to bring twice as many as Alan.

How many sheep did each of the children bring home?

(*Just a real-life everyday story of country folk.*)

One answer. From Mike (Figure 7.3).

From this written evidence, it looks like Mike used 'trial and adjust' though not overly intuitively (Figure 7.4).

Second answer. From Peter.

I said read the question carefully! I could defend Peter's interpretation, especially if he knew anything about sheep farming. At least he ended up with whole sheep after some worrying moments on the way. Good algebra though.

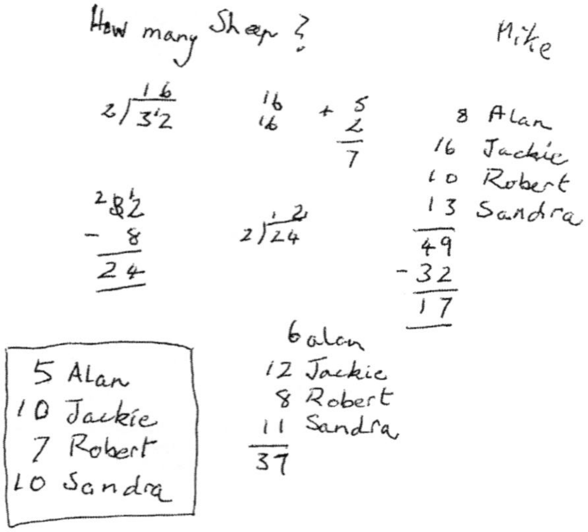

How many Sheep?   Mike

$\begin{array}{r} 16 \\ 2\overline{)3'2} \end{array}$ $\begin{array}{r} 16 \\ 16 \\ +\ \underline{5} \\ 7 \end{array}$ 8 Alan
16 Jackie
10 Robert
13 Sandra

$\begin{array}{r} 2\ 8\frac{1}{2} \\ -\ \underline{8} \\ 24 \end{array}$ $2\overline{)2\ 4}$ $\begin{array}{r} 49 \\ -32 \\ \overline{17} \end{array}$

6 alan
12 Jackie
8 Robert
11 Sandra
$\overline{37}$

5 Alan
10 Jackie
7 Robert
10 Sandra

Figure 7.3 Mike's answer.

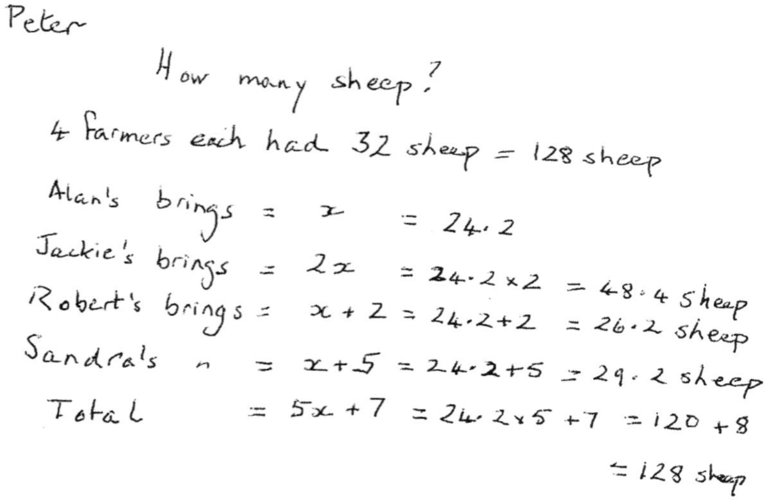

Peter

How many sheep?

4 farmers each had 32 sheep = 128 sheep

Alan's brings = x = 24.2

Jackie's brings = $2x$ = 24.2 × 2 = 48.4 sheep

Robert's brings = $x + 2$ = 24.2 + 2 = 26.2 sheep

Sandra's " = $x + 5$ = 24.2 + 5 = 29.2 sheep

Total = $5x + 7$ = 24.2 × 5 + 7 = 120 + 8

= 128 sheep

Figure 7.4 Peter's answer.

I asked the teachers from the maths department of that very prestigious school to mark the two students' work out of 10. One teacher gave Mike a 2 and Pete a 10. Another teacher gave Mike a 6 and Pete a 0. The teachers did ask for a mark scheme. I didn't provide one; 'No. I want your professional judgement'.

The curriculum and cognitive style

In 2001, Irish and Dutch colleagues and three teachers from my UK school published a paper on the cognitive style of 9- to 13-year-old pupils from mainstream and specialist schools in our countries. The research was carried out in 1999 when the Irish curriculum was very prescriptive and very inchworm. We found that both the mainstream and the dyslexic pupils from Ireland showed a much higher proportion of inchworms than for the other two countries. Sometimes you get what you teach. Sometimes that may be not good. The maths pedagogy in Ireland did change radically around 2000 from dictating one method to much more flexible cognition. The way we teach has implications for the way our learners learn. Of course.

As I have already hinted, there is a great attraction for learners in using algorithms and procedures. The benefits of using algorithms were listed by Usiskin (1998):

Power: An algorithm applies to a class of problems.

Reliability and accuracy: Done correctly, an algorithm always provides the correct answer. *(That may be optimistic.)*

Speed: An algorithm proceeds directly to the answer.

A record: A paper-and-pencil algorithm provides a record of how the answer was determined.

That does tie in nicely with some pedagogies.

Mind maps

Mind maps help some learners to get their ideas on paper. The order in which the ideas are generated doesn't matter. The mind map can act like a brainstorming session. Tony Buzan introduced mind maps during a 1974 BBC TV series he hosted, called *Use Your Head*. I have always believed that this strategy is great for grasshoppers, less so for inchworms, who tend to prefer lists. However, I do like the way a mind map can precede a list and help inchworm learners to construct their list. They also work well for spotting links and patterns. It's another example of using flexible learning strategies to achieve goals.

Interactions between cognitive style and other learning factors

Cognitive influences on learning are rarely stand-alone. For example, an inchworm style for mental arithmetic might just about work if the student has very strong short-term and working memories and rapid retrieval of number facts. Without strengths in those three areas, the student is going to fail at mental arithmetic. A student with a grasshopper style and those accompanying problems may still survive most questions by using more (mentally) efficient methods.

Grasshoppers are often disinclined to document their methods. Their processing may be too fast for them to be aware of all that happened in their brain or they may not want to admit to using a method that was not taught and thus maybe not endorsed by the teacher or an examination mark scheme. The UK examination culture is to 'show your working'. You get marks for 'showing your working' even if the answer is wrong. You could pass an exam without getting a correct answer if you 'show your working'. I'm not so sure that is a great lesson for life. Keeps inchworms happy (especially if they are the examiners).

I know it was a long time ago, but the memory is still fresh. My maths teacher used to pick me up by my ear if I missed out any step in writing my method in my exercise book. My right ear bears witness to this re-education to an inchworm style. Early learning experiences again.

An inchworm style is not conducive to estimation (see Footnote). Maybe it's about not seeing the big picture. So back to 97 and 100:

A student who interprets numbers literally (or the mathematical equivalent to literal) will be disadvantaged, especially in mental arithmetic. Once again, we should look back at the early experiences of learning maths. An over-emphasis on rote learning facts will tend to encourage an inchworm cognitive style. To round numbers, as in rounding 97 to 100 (which is also an estimate for 97), the learner has to have some understanding (or at least a visual image) of where a specific number fits among other numbers and to understand how a two-digit number can relate to a three-digit number. Place value. So sometimes the question will involve counting back 3 or 4. I met a 30-something-year-old artist who explained that she used this method if the counting back was 1 or 2 but 3 or more was too much. That is working memory yet again.

Let me leave that two-digit/three-digit thought hanging there and pick it up again in Chapter 11, which deals with materials and visual images.

It seems to be stating the obvious, but I am sure that teaching to develop a flexible cognitive style helps in understanding and linking the concepts of maths. As ever, there is a caution, a necessary awareness, that choice can make some students anxious. These (usually) inchworm cognitive style students want just one method and it must be as universal as possible.

Implications for teaching and learning

A couple of extra thoughts and observations may be apposite as a finishing flourish to this chapter.

I have long been nervous of the scenario where pupils sit around a table and discover 'things' for themselves. I am less wary of guided discovery, but, then, when does the guided bit overwhelm the discovery bit? (That's a great topic for discussion.) What worries me is how this is handled. I think that these discovery sessions need very close and frequent monitoring just in case the pupils discover the wrong thing and that discovery has enough time to get into the brain. Remember the problem with the dominant influence of the first experience of a new learning?

But, then, I want to encourage discussions around 'Can we think of another way of doing this? Can we see this from a different perspective? Why did you do it that way?' I think this should be an obligatory metacognition part of the classroom ethos.

And, then, it is worth keeping in mind that maths is developmental. This tells us that learning should be, too. As learners seek solutions, we as teachers should be as aware as we can be of the knowledge, and ignorance, they bring to the problem. This is another reason to build in frequent reviews of the knowledge and concepts that might be pertinent to the development of the new knowledge. Teaching should be mindful of where the topic has come from and where it is going (see Chapter 3). Short cuts may work for the moment, for the one topic being taught at that time, but they may not set foundations for future work.

Footnote

You'll notice that this chapter doesn't mention maths learning difficulties. As with all topics in this book, it's about everyone.

Aboriginal languages from around the Uluru area have words for only one, two, three, many and few. So the 36 (massive)-rock formation, Kata Tjuta, near Uluru, translates to 'many heads'. I like that as an estimate. Deals with any possibility of someone discovering another rock. When visiting that area, I asked my guide how they conveyed distances when they set off to visit another settlement. He explained that they used the phrase 'Little bit long way'. That has got to be my favourite estimate expression of all time. Great for using to explain to children how far a car journey is going to be.

It's sale time in my hometown as I write this and notices in shop windows claim '70% off. 20% extra off today'. I think that many shoppers take a sort of grasshopper approach and simply decide that 'That's a lot off'. An appropriate estimation in the circumstances. And I do like the precursor for these offers: 'Up to'.

Chapter 8

Linking facts and concepts

Once again, I'm visiting one of my most influential sources of inspiration. And to remind you that it is one that is evidence-based.

That major study *How People Learn* (2000) came up with three Key Findings about learning plus an awful lot more good stuff. As you know by now, I think all three findings are very pertinent to maths education. The Second Finding sets the tenor for this chapter:

Key Finding 2

To develop confidence in an area of inquiry, students must:

(a) *have a deep foundation of factual knowledge,*
(b) *understand facts and ideas in the context of a conceptual framework, and*
(c) *organise knowledge in ways that facilitate retrieval and application.*

Although in many of my lectures to special educational needs (SEN) teachers I've included this finding as key to helping and understanding struggling learners, I use it as part of the philosophy of this book because it was written for all learners. As ever, we should be thinking about working across the whole of the normal distribution.

Key Finding 2 is almost a song, 'It ain't what you know, it's the way that you use it. That's what gets results'.

Let's look at the parts of this finding, starting with 'Students must have a deep foundation of factual knowledge'. That's one of my worries. It's not that I disagree, rather I worry that some educators stop there and don't get to the next two bits.

'Deep foundation' and how it is interpreted can be a problem for many learners in maths, particularly those with poor number sense. This can start at the earliest stages of learning (for example, subitising, the ability to quantify a small (up to 5) random set of dots without counting them).

I want to talk about this 'deep foundation'. Maths is a wonderful subject for using what you know to work out what you don't know. Facts link and concepts link, much more than in many other subjects. So we might be able to do something about that rather challenging 'deep' bit. A bonus for learners is that the 'something' that we can do for the factual bits can also enhance their understanding of maths. It's that 'What else are you teaching?' again.

Here's an example I have mentioned before: What I have found over the years is that the number facts that are most likely to be the foundation knowledge for many children and adults are based on 1, 2, 5, 10, 20, 50 and so on. It can't be a coincidence that coinage in many countries is based on these values. For example, I've yet to come across a $7 coin or note (forgery alert).

You will notice that a consequence of knowing this is that I devote quite a bit of space to addressing the reality of a poor or slow retrieval of facts (or both) throughout this book.

Some students will link facts intuitively. For example, if $5 + 5 = 10$, then $5 + 6 = 11$. This 'doubles $+/- 1$' strategy was encouraged in the UK's National Numeracy Strategy (1999). Linking just wasn't developed as far as it might have been, such as this more sophisticated example from a 13-year-old who went on to achieve an A* in General Certificate of Secondary Education (GCSE) maths. He knew the 'square fact', $6 \times 6 = 36$, and worked out for himself that 3×6 was half of 6×6 and thus got his answer of 18. Using what you know to work out what you don't know gives a security which will be stronger, and often quicker, than trying to retrieve seemingly unconnected facts from memory.

And, in an example where the school had not asked or shown a pupil, 'What to do when you can't', I once worked with a 10-year-old who told me that he couldn't remember basic subtraction facts, so his school gave him 5 minutes to practise these at the start of every lesson. No improvement. No motivation. I showed him how to count on to find a subtraction fact. It was a solution for him. Linking addition and subtraction was the bonus. And he didn't have 5 minutes of failure at the start of his maths lessons. It wasn't a sophisticated strategy but it worked for him and a barrier was removed. This was teaching maths as it is to the learner as he is. I would want him to progress from just counting on in ones, but the message was 'There are other ways you can do things'. And they are mathematical.

When prospective students came to my school for their interview, I used to ask, 'How are you getting on with the times tables? Which ones to you reckon you really, really know?' So so many times the answer was 'I know my 2s, my 5s and my 10s'. Some would add to this, 'and my 0s and 1s'. I've been asking teachers at my training sessions if they too had experienced this. It's a common experience in many schools. Probably with adults, too, since you're not likely to practise the 7 times table when you're, say, 31. So those 1, 2, 5, 10 facts have to suffice as the deep foundation of factual knowledge for the other times tables and basic facts that I need to use in my teaching.

Students must understand facts and ideas in the context of a conceptual framework

Maths is a great subject for this part of Key Finding 2. Let me give you an example. I'll touch on times table facts yet again. I have more on this in Chapter 5. Keep in mind the 'What else are you teaching?' question.

I reckon that the hardest fact from the times table collection is 7×6. Could be 7×8. Let me start by addressing this fact (or these facts, again).

Multiplication facts seem to be a challenge to many students and adults. If rote learning, even if put to the best music possible, doesn't work, then a maths strategy may give the answer.

The first contextual and conceptual foundation is that multiplication is repeated addition. This links together add and multiply with 'lots of'. Thus,

$$7 \times 6 = 6 + 6 + 6 + 6 + 6 + 6 + 6.$$

The next contextual fact is that 7 is 5 + 2. Remember that 2 and 5 are core numbers for memories? And, do you remember the visual image for 7 as 5 plus 2?

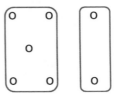

By the way, what I'm doing for 7 × 6 applies to 7 × 8.

$$\text{So } 7 \times 6 = 5 \times 6 + 2 \times 6 \text{ and } 7 \times 8 = 5 \times 8 + 2 \times 8.$$

You've probably realised that this applies to 7 times any number. This links the number facts to algebra, giving us:

$$7 \times a = 5 \times a + 2 \times a \quad \text{or} \quad 7a = 5a + 2a.$$

Students organise knowledge in ways that facilitate retrieval and application

The organising of the knowledge here is to link addition and multiplication and to use partial products to find the final product. It is an example of generalising.

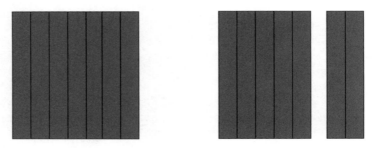

Figure 8.1 Seven lots of six is five lots of six (30) plus two lots of six (12). $7 \times 6 = 30 + 12 = 42$.

The illustrations show Cuisenaire rods being used as visual (and kinaesthetic) models for 7 × 6 and 7 × 8. They are area models, generalised as $y = ab$ and also as $y = a(c + d)$.

A further link here is to division and understanding that it is the inverse or opposite operation to multiplication and thus seen as repeated subtraction. So 56 ÷ 8 is 'How many lots of 8 can I subtract from 56?' Doing this in partial products:

Subtract 5 lots of 8   56 − 40 = 16
Subtract 2 lots of 8   16 − 16 = 0
So 56 ÷ 8 = 7.

This strategy sets the foundations for 'long' division. It is another example of 'What else are you teaching?' And it links multiplication and division.

Figure 8.2 Seven lots of eight is five lots of eight (40) plus two lots of eight (16). $7 \times 8 =$ 40 + 16 = 56.

The Bruner progression for this would see the rods being replaced by images of rectangles (an area model) and then by symbols. As you know by now, I like the symbols to be present, alongside the materials and the visuals, at every stage.

Facts: Right, wrong and inferior

I looked up 'fact' on the web just to be sure that I understood exactly what it meant.

> A fact is something that has become known as true. A fact is, then, a statement of an epistemological quality that is founded, which makes it superior to an opinion or an interpretation.

I think that helped to form my opinion.

The bad news for many of my students, then, is that their opinion that $7 \times 6 = 48$ is inferior to the fact that $7 \times 6 = 42$. In fact, it's worse than inferior, it's wrong. It's not even a valid interpretation. Feedback can be harsh.

Fractions, decimals and percentages

These three concepts are inter-linked, although they are not always taught with that in mind. They can be mutually supportive. In the book I wrote with my colleague Richard Ashcroft, *Mathematics for Dyslexics*, first published in 1993 and now in its fourth edition, we had a chapter that gave an overview of the three concepts together, before the next three chapters which addressed fractions, decimals and percentages as single topics. The goal was to make understanding each of the three topics mutually supportive.

Figure 8.3 shows the link between fractions, decimals and percentages as a way of sequencing fractions in order of their value.

Not surprisingly, Dienes/base-ten blocks provide helpful images of the base-ten system. But they are also effective for percentages, decimals and fractions. If we can use the same images in different parts of maths, then it can only enhance the linking of concepts and literally illustrate the developmental nature of maths.

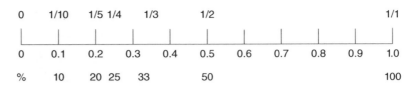

Figure 8.3 The number line for fractions, decimals and percentages.

I am going to use the 100-square to develop another image of the link between fractions, decimals and percentages. The sequence of Figures 8.4 to 8.11 shows this without a great need for words.

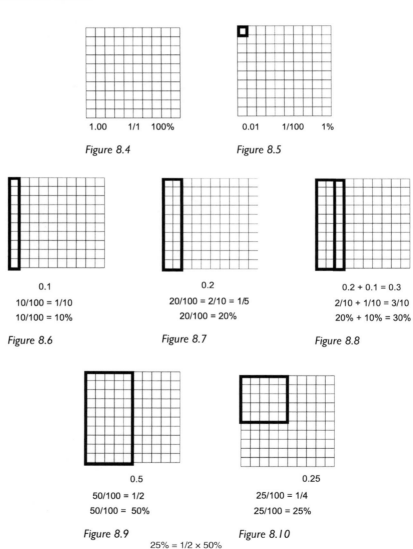

1.00   1/1   100%

Figure 8.4

0.01   1/100   1%

Figure 8.5

0.1

10/100 = 1/10

10/100 = 10%

Figure 8.6

0.2

20/100 = 2/10 = 1/5

20/100 = 20%

Figure 8.7

0.2 + 0.1 = 0.3

2/10 + 1/10 = 3/10

20% + 10% = 30%

Figure 8.8

0.5

50/100 = 1/2

50/100 = 50%

Figure 8.9

0.25

25/100 = 1/4

25/100 = 25%

Figure 8.10

25% = 1/2 × 50%

1/4 = 1/2 × 1/2

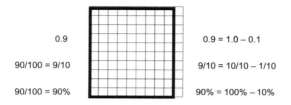

0.9

90/100 = 9/10

90/100 = 90%

0.9 = 1.0 – 0.1

9/10 = 10/10 – 1/10

90% = 100% – 10%

Figure 8.11

Directed questions can be used to explore these images and their inter-connections. For example, 'What is the link between ½ and ¼?' and 'Can there be percentages that are more than 100?' and 'Why isn't 2/10 +1/10 equal to 3/20?'

For thoughts on linking basic arithmetic to algebra, see Chapter 4. This link also shows the importance of the foundations, the early learning and later the re-learning.

Chapter 9

The role of language, vocabulary and symbols

Communication and perspectives on communication

You will find some overlap between this chapter and other bits of this book, but I wanted to collect in one chapter some related factors and influences around language and symbols. The overlap is partly because these factors are so pervasive, and so important, in maths. The overlap happens most in Chapter 10 on inconsistencies and Chapter 5 on topics that create the most difficulty, one of those topics being word problems. Maths has many links and overlaps, which is both a good thing and a bad thing, depending on how they are handled. Hurdles or bridges. Partly, this is a chapter of quirky observations that I hope will highlight and maybe clarify more aspects of maths. Underlying this goal is a belief that before you make things complicated you need to make them simple.

Richard Skemp succinctly summed up the role and importance of symbols:

> A symbol is a sound, or something visible, mentally connected to an idea. This idea is the meaning of the symbol. Without an idea attached, a symbol is empty, meaningless.

That observation applies to reading as well as to maths.

Communication is a crucial component in any subject. In early maths, communication mostly uses objects and words. Symbols are introduced a little later. Sometimes the connections between the number of objects and the names and symbols for those quantities are straightforward, sometimes not. Whilst maths symbols usually have consistency (for example, pi is always π), the words associated with symbols, especially in basic maths, can be inconsistent and often nuanced. For example, word problems sometimes put words in contexts where they relate to a different symbol. For instance, 'more' generally infers + but not always: 'Jan has 6 more medals than Mic. If Jan has 9 medals, how many does Mic have?' This negates the simplistic problem-solving strategy of 'Circle the numbers and the operation word. Then solve'.

I like Skemp's warning that without an attached idea a symbol is empty and meaningless. This seems to me to be a strong caution about an over-reliance on rote learning. Instead, it is an encouragement to use visual images and the inter-linking of ideas and facts in early maths to give meaning to the symbols. I want to add to this a caution that sometimes learners use the wrong idea because they have yet to reach a new, more developed context which supplies a new perspective. For example, a relatively frequent error from my 15-minute standardised test to the item $2y + 5 = 31$ was 6. The reason? $26 + 5 = 31$. That's reasonable if you've not met algebra. In a similar vein, up to meeting algebra, pupils have met x for multiply and then need to adjust for $\times$, the unknown, in an algebra context. Using a curly **x** might help.

During an informal diagnosis, I asked a (14-year-old) student, 'What is half of 50?' She replied '25'. A little later, I showed her '½ × 50' written on paper. She said she didn't know the answer, but of course she did know the answer, she didn't know the symbols. I mention linking quite a lot in this book (for example, linking materials to symbols and linking words and symbols). Interestingly, in terms of words and symbols, this girl spoke six languages. I do like the concept of multiple intelligences, especially the bit about not having them all at the same intensity.

I tried to minimise the use of language in the 15-minute standardised test in my diagnosis book, *More Trouble with Maths*. It was a case of 'What are you testing?' I was not primarily testing word problems or maths vocabulary. But I was testing symbols.

In teaching, visual images and materials can help explanations that often are biased towards the restricted use of symbols and words. Appropriately chosen, they can clarify ideas that might otherwise be abstract and help to retain them in long-term memory.

Inconsistencies and too much information (also see Chapter 10)

Number sense includes the ability to name quantities and link them to symbols. Initially, this will mean connecting the quantity to the name and the symbol for a single digit. The task for the child then progresses to being able to put the names and digits from 0 to 9 into a correct sequence. After 9, the child has to deal with the same ten symbols, which are then combined in pairs to make the numbers from 10 to 99, then to make three-digit numbers from 100 to 999 and thus onwards to numbers with 4, 5, 6 digits and beyond. These digits must be in the right order for each individual number. For ten, 10, we use the 1 digit followed by the 0 digit. Maybe it's because ten is such a familiar number we don't consider any confusion is possible, but the language we use has to be specific. For example, 'one and zero' could mean $1 + 0 = 1$ because we often use 'and' to mean add. And it has been known for multiplication by ten to be described as 'Add a zero'. Not good for $3.7 × 10$.

Zero is a tricky concept. Small behaviours and experiences can confirm this belief for children. For example, when young children count forwards to 10, they usually start with 1, but when they count back from 10, they end at 0.

Unfortunately, the names, in English, for the first two-digit numbers are exceptions. 'Eleven' and 'twelve' are one-offs and the teen number names have their syllables in the inverse order; for example, fifteen (five ten) is written as 15 (ten five). I have also found that pupils can confuse the similar-sounding words 'twelve' and 'twenty' or 'thirteen' and 'thirty'.

When I think about '20th century', I need to inhibit the 20 and write, for example, 1964 as nineteen sixty-four. And, when I had my 49th birthday, I was starting my 50th year, but when asked how old I am, I would say, of course, 'Forty-nine'. There is, of course, a logic to these two examples, but my brain sometimes takes the easy way to interpret numbers.

Pupils need to remember that words they use outside maths may have different meanings when used within maths. This phenomenon is much more prevalent in early maths. For example, 'take away' can refer to a meal you take out of the restaurant or it can mean subtraction. For the meal, a 'take away' has become a thing, a name, whereas 'take away' in maths is an operation, something you do. I often think that there are too many words for each of the four operations to be of any help in developing understanding through consistency, but the positive interpretation is that this situation can be used to enhance understanding. For example, in my attempt to rehabilitate 'take away', I could argue that 'subtraction' is abstract in comparison with 'take away' and thus 'take away' could be used to give meaning to subtraction. 'Minus' can cause problems, too. As in 'minus a minus'!

Figure 9.1 Sign from South Africa.

I have a long list of polysemous terms, words and terms that have multiple meanings, in all four editions of my book, *The Trouble with Maths*.

Choice can create stress in learners and this obviously includes the choice of words used for each of the four operation symbols and for the = symbol (Figure 9.1).

Where to go? Food or maths? Do I need to do a subtraction before I can order my food?

Potentially, confusion can arise from different mathematical meanings for the same word (for example, fourth used as an ordinal number or as a fraction).

We add up and write the answer down. I guess that, when told to add a column of numbers up, most pupils add down, from top number to bottom number.

Homophones

A teacher at one of my lectures gave me this wonderful example from an 8-year-old pupil for 'two lines of symmetry'. (Almost a homophone!) (Figure 9.2.)

Hidden symbols

I'm pretty sure that the way we use symbols to write fractions contributes to their reputation as being 'difficult/impossible'. For example, Figure 9.3 shows how $1 \div 5$ becomes one fifth, $\frac{1}{5}$, by hiding the dots in the division symbol. This can be exacerbated by reading the fraction as 'one over five' and not mentioning division.

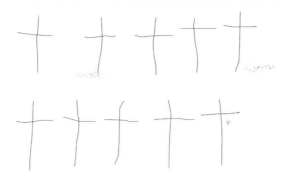

Figure 9.2 'Two lines in a cemetery'.

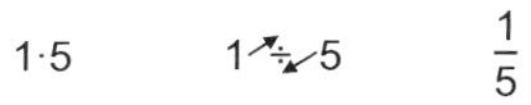

$$1\cdot5 \qquad 1\diagup5 \qquad \frac{1}{5}$$

Figure 9.3 The hidden symbol for division.

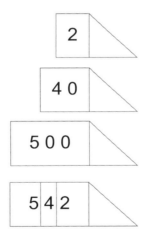

Figure 9.4 Place value cards.

Another example of confusion with the language around fractions: 2/3 can be said as 'two thirds', which doesn't mean a dead heat for third place from two competitors. These examples are not helpful in explaining fractions.

For basic facts, we sometimes say, for example, 'six fives', which means 6 × 5 in that multiplication context. In algebra, we write ab, which means 'a multiplied by b'. Perhaps a × b would be as confusing, especially if it's a × rather than a x. Brackets can be used to imply multiplication. For example, 6(3 + 5) = 6 × 3 + 6 × 5 and 6(a + b) means 6a + 6b.

And now that I'm on a roll, our place value system hides symbols. For example, we do not write 57 as $5 \times 10 + 7 \times 1$ or 213 as $2 \times 100 + 1 \times 10 + 3 \times 1$. The language we use for numbers can confuse, too. For example, 748 can be said as 'seven hundred and forty-eight' and then literally interpreted as 700408', or 'fifty thousand and sixty' might be written as 5000060.

Place value 'arrow' cards might help with writing numbers in symbols when they are said in words (for example, as in Figure 9.4). The cards are placed on top of each other to make, as shown here, 542, thus allowing the hidden place value zeros to be revealed.

What about when we ask, 'How many 6s in 72?' A literal interpretation could be 'I only see a 7 and a 2' and not interpret the symbols as $72 \div 6$, which incidentally reverses the order of 6 and 72 as written in 'How many 6s in 72?'

Figure 9.5, given to me by a teacher on one of my training courses in Singapore, shows the pupil being successful with every format except the missing symbol one.

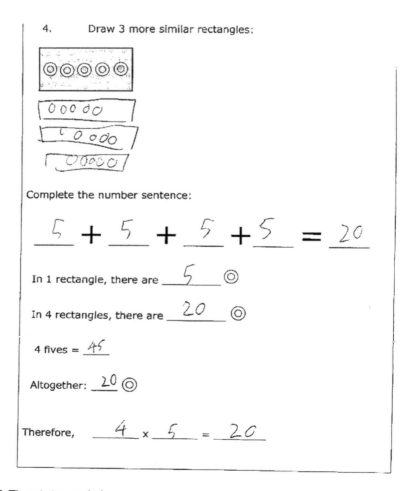

Figure 9.5 The missing symbol.

Confusing symbols

I have a confession about the first edition of my first book on maths and dyslexia. I didn't notice that in the proofs of the chapter on division the ÷ symbol had blurred into the + symbol. That was confusing. I got it right in the subsequent editions. It's easy to write symbols carelessly; for example, a slight rotation of + could cause it to be interpreted as an x.

The order and font size used for maths terms can confuse some learners, as happens sometimes in dyslexia, where, for example, 'was' is written as 'saw'. So 2^3 is not 23. Crack the code! 2b is not b^2 and b^2 is not b_2, but ab = ba. More code. The answer to the question 'Which is the bigger number, 3 or 8?', when shown as visual images, is one of the probes for diagnosing dyscalculia in a well-known online assessment.

Sometimes it's a previous interpretation of a symbol, which is no longer relevant in a new situation. A relatively common error from students for this 'bus stop' division item,

$$10\overline{)8020}$$

is 82, created when the symbols are interpreted as, "How many tens in 80?" '8'. "How many tens in twenty?" '2' It's an example of an early method being used literally and inappropriately. Plus the learner needs to interpret the 'bus stop' presentation as meaning division.

Linked to this is the subtraction mantra 'Take the little number from the big number'. When I was assessing that gifted linguist, the 14-year-old girl who spoke six languages, I showed her this subtraction, which she answered '51'. I asked her to explain her method and she answered, 'Oh. I've done it again! I just take away the number that's more comfortable for me'.

$$\begin{array}{r} 75 \\ -26 \\ \hline \end{array}$$

Some things mathematicians do with two lines.

+add   = equals   × multiply   > greater than   < smaller than

|| parallel   and, a little leeway here :   ≈ approximately equal to

Confusing, misleading and quick-fix instructions

I guess I could have included 'Take the little number from the big number' in this section. I think a particularly worrying example is the mantra often used for multiplying and dividing by powers of ten, 'Move the decimal point' and 'Add a zero (or zeros)'. For example, to multiply by 1000, count the number of zeros, 3, and move the decimal point that many times (hopefully in the right direction) or just write 3 zeros at the end of the number. Potential disaster there. A frequent error from my standardised maths test for the item 'Multiply 4.68×1000' was '4068'. Using the 'move the decimal point' mantra means that three moves are needed, but only two digits are available, so many of the students in the sample slipped a zero into the space left by the decimal point when it moved. I would want to lead my students to a method based on the concept of place value, by considering what happens to 4 when you multiply it by 1000 and hoping they answer 'Four thousand' and then write 4000. They can then write the number with all the relevant digits in the same sequence (4.68) to give 4680, checking that the 4 still represents 4000.

Two of the most (easily) remembered quick-fix rules? To divide by a fraction, 'Don't ask why, just turn upside down and multiply'. I love the disclaimer 'Don't ask why'.

'Minus a minus makes a plus'. If you say so. In other words, 'Don't ask why'. But maybe to get the rhyme and follow the style, use 'Don't make a fuss. Minus a minus makes a plus'.

Let me know if you use it with your students.

Chapter 10

The inconsistencies of maths and their impact on learning

Some of the topics and perspectives that I think are critical influences on the way we should teach maths have an impact on a broad range of topics. Hence, I find myself returning to some of these aspects in different settings. What I am trying to do in this chapter is gather pertinent examples and focus on the impact of inconsistencies and their influence on learning maths.

A substantial amount of research suggests that the early learning experiences for maths have a long-lasting influence on future learning (for example, Geary, 2015).

> Children who start school without a solid understanding of number words, numerals, and the quantities they represent are at heightened risk for poor mathematics achievement throughout schooling and as a result, poor employment-relevant quantitative skills.

Among my concerns deriving from this is that large group of students who have experienced or endured maybe eight or nine years of maths education in schools to no significant effect. The Geary quote alone emphasises the importance of addressing those early topics, those foundations, in maths – no matter what the age of the learner – and in an age-appropriate way.

I want to highlight some of the inconsistencies in early maths because of their potential to confuse learners unless we teach such topics with a full awareness of their potential to confuse and consequently to demotivate.

> The desire for consistency is a central motivator of our behaviour.
>
> (*Influence*, Cialdini, 2007)

Some examples of inconsistencies and potential confusions

Teen numbers

In the English language, the teen numbers (and eleven and twelve) – a learner's first experience of place value – are exceptions because they are inconsistent: 15 is 'fifteen' and 19 is 'nineteen'. The teen/ten comes second in the word but is the first digit when the number is represented as symbols. The situation improves after twenty. Obviously, the order in which information is presented influences learning.

This is not the case in all languages (for example, Welsh and Cantonese). Connie Ho, a researcher from Hong Kong, whose work is outstanding, has found that the consistency of Cantonese gives learners an initial boost but this diminishes as they go further in maths. That is likely to be the consequence of appropriate teaching and the support of having information in a second language. I mention this to give a perspective on what I am saying in this chapter.

Sounds like

The -teen and -ty numbers (for example, thirteen and thirty) sound similar. The ending 'th' in fractions such as hundredth is close to silent and can confuse (see below).

Sequences

1, 2, 3, 4, 5… is a sequence that is getting bigger in value, but 1/1, 1/2, 1/3, 1/4, 1/5… is a sequence that is getting smaller in value.

Fractions and ordinal numbers

Third can be 1/3 or a position in a race. Fifth can be 1/5 or a position in a series (ordinality), so 'th' can imply a fraction or a position in an order.

Fractions

I like the idea of a fraction in its 'simplest form'. Many of my students found 'simplest' hard to come to terms with. It needs some explaining to go alongside the demands of computations and a knowledge of the relevant basic facts. An equivalent fraction is created when we multiply by 1, but related previous learning may have lodged in the brain, telling the learner that multiplying by 1 does not change the number. Equivalent fractions are about change but also about keeping the same value.

The rules for fractions on how we treat denominators and numerators in subtraction and addition as opposed to multiplication could be viewed as inconsistent. As for division…

Patterns for 6

My thoughts on representing 6 visually are based on using the core numbers, 1 and 5. The 6 on playing cards, dice and dominoes is not about 1 and 5 but about 2 and 3. For playing cards, 7, 8 and 9 are then based on 5 plus 2, 3 or 4; 6 is an exception, an inconsistency.

Six.   o   o   o   o   o

            o   o   OR   o

            o   o   o   o

There's a decision here. Both illustrations are valid, and we do need to encourage different ways of seeing numbers. The 5 + 1 version for 6 serves a concept that can be used to develop a range of maths skills. So do we restrict our image of 6 to the 5 + 1 version or do we encourage flexibility? We need to do both, appropriately and without confusing learners or limiting their thinking.

The commutative property

It works for addition $(5 + 7 = 7 + 5)$ and for multiplication $(3 \times 9 = 9 \times 3)$ but not for subtraction $(7 - 5 \neq 5 - 7)$ or for division $(27 \div 3 \neq 27 \div 9)$. Visual images and manipulatives can be used to help to explain that.

Coins

I like to use coins sometimes as visual support for numbers, but they are not always consistent. For example, in the US, the dime (10c) is smaller than the nickel (5c). In Australia, the $2 coin is smaller than the $1 coin. This is counterintuitive. Visual images are better when they are intuitive. As so many aspects of society accelerate, one of which is paying electronically by card, coinage is much less a part of everyday life. Australia no longer issues 1c and 2c coins, which limits the use of coinage for teaching maths. The UK has considered losing the 1p and 2p coins. At the other extreme, in 2015, the Zimbabwean 100-trillion-dollar note was worth 40 US cents. Was it an extra long note in order to fit on all those zeros?

The US coin for a quarter of a dollar (25c) is, reasonably, called a 'quarter'. Maybe this is the reason why some students write 'quarter after three' as '3.25', although I have seen UK students do this, too. Maybe a quarter of 100, rather than a quarter of 60, is the dominant entry in the brain. By the way, maybe some learners would prefer it if there were 100° in a right angle. The reason it's not 100 is in the choice of 360° for one revolution; 360 is divisible by every number from 1 to 10, except 7. We don't need the 7x facts here, then.

Words for operations

I was doing some training in a primary school and asked the teachers what word (or words) they used for the procedure we use in subtraction when a digit in the number we are subtracting (subtrahend) is bigger than the digit in the number we are subtracting from (minuend). They told me that, between them, the terms they used in their classes were 'renaming', 'borrow and pay back', 'decomposing', 'trading' and 'regrouping'. Not all of them were used in the one class, but in each class it was a different word. The teachers were not aware of this. It must have taken some pupils a while to catch on to the new name when they changed class.

Decimal numbers

Look at this sequence:

> thousands hundreds tens ones tenths hundredths thousandths

Students, with a sense of symmetry, have asked me, "Where is the 'oneth'?" Sometimes the decimal point exerts too much influence on developing the concept of decimals. It is not the centre of symmetry.

What's a thousandth of a thousand?

I mentioned this next bit in Chapter 9 on vocabulary and language, but I had a student who alerted me, unintentionally, to the similarity in sound between 'hundreds' and 'hundredths' (and so on). The 'th' sound is almost silent. Communications skills sometimes can require over-emphasis. The almost-silent 'th' blocked his understanding of decimal numbers.

Algebra and symbols

Algebra is, of course, very much about symbols. Sometimes it is about symbols that are not there. For example, ab means $a \times b$ and $4(a - b)$ means $4 \times a - 4 \times b$. Sometimes it's about where a symbol or number is placed and the font size (for example, $2a$ and a^2). This is just another reason to use clear text for students.

Time

Time offers many examples of what appear to be inconsistencies. It uses base 12 for hours. There are 60 minutes in an hour and 60 seconds in a minute. The 24-hour clock confuses; for example, '20.30 is the same time as 8.30 pm'.

Changing the order in which the information is presented is an inconsistency for learners who have directional problems. For example, 'twenty past six' and 'six twenty' and we say 'five past one' and write 1.05.

We sometimes count up to the next hour instead of counting down from the last hour, so 'twenty to nine' is more likely than 'forty minutes after eight'. Interpreting 'eight forty' requires subtracting 40 from 60 in order to work out that there are 20 minutes left before the new hour. I like the idea in time that the tipping point for going from counting on to counting down is the half hour. That idea has mileage. I use a version in my sloping number line.

Sometimes learners need to inhibit previous learning to get past the seemingly inconsistent nature of some maths. 'If you say so!' They may well need teacher awareness and input to recognise and address this situation.

Chapter 11

How to use materials and visual images

I have such a strong commitment to the appropriate use of materials and visual images that I want to start this chapter with a statement of intent.

For the first 14 years of my teaching career in schools, I taught physics. I showed my students experiments designed to illustrate a concept. That was the norm. It also introduced a degree of uncertainty and schadenfreude into my lessons. 'Would the experiment work?' My (rhetorical) question then is 'Why don't we do more of this to illustrate and explain maths concepts?' My maths classroom had a small adjoining room. That room was full of maths kit, ready to use, sometimes for demonstrations I had planned and sometimes in response to a need that cropped up in the lesson.

Numicon have done a great deal to encourage the use of materials and manipulatives in schools worldwide. My commitment here was as lead author for their *Big Ideas* publication. I want to encourage this way of teaching, too, and to extend that encouragement to a much greater use of appropriate visual images in lessons, especially when we now have great information technology tools at our disposal.

A great deal of what I say in this chapter isn't new, just a new perspective. I have used that approach several times already. Sometimes in teaching we are susceptible to fashions without validating them. There is more call these days for interventions and ideas to be 'evidence-based'. I hope such evidence is from sound research from large samples. Sometimes we let great ideas slip out of use until someone rediscovers them. For example, Hattie's book *Visible Learning* has given Piaget a boost, ranking Piagetian programmes second in effectiveness out of 133 classroom interventions. Piaget was a big influence in education when I started teaching in schools in the late 1960s. (Then less so.) And Bruner was too.

It would make this book rather large if I gave every example of the uses of visuals and materials, so I have been selective and, I hope, representative. Much more can be seen in the video tutorials in my website www.mathsexplained.co.uk.

A quick overview and critique of those 'old ideas'

Let's start with Piaget. Here are two observations from the perspective of this book.

First, pretty much every time I look at cylindrical(ish) containers in a supermarket, I feel Piaget leaning over me and asking whether I can compare the volumes. And that's before I get my purchase home, open it and find it's barely ¾ full (estimating with fractions!). I know that Piaget's theory of conservation is being used against me. Not to be arrogant, but I am meant to teach this stuff, so if that makes me confused, what does it do to young learners when faced with conservation tasks?

One of the two key basic tasks used to check out dyscalculia is subitising, the ability to look at a small cluster (5 or fewer) of randomly organised dots and know how many there are. The spacing between these dots must bring Piaget into the task.

The second observation concerns Piaget's four stages of cognitive development. The last stage, the formal operational stage, is meant to click in at age 12 years and up. My experience from the outliers and the low achievers is that 12 years old is too soon for us teachers to give up on using visual images, particularly when they are used alongside the symbols. I'm not sure whether there is any age I would pick as a cut-off. I like to keep the normal distribution and individual variations in mind. And I like visuals. Consequently, I like to use the formal operational and concrete or visual operational stages together, at the same time, in a mutually supportive way.

UK maths educator Kath Hart said that when she wrote her autobiography it would be titled *Bricks are Bricks and Sums are Sums*, based on her experience of pupils rarely connecting the two. I think that new technology allows us to present visual images alongside the symbols and thus maximise the chance of learners connecting the two. It's a case of 'It ain't what you do, it's the way that you do it'. Skemp emphasised the huge importance of symbols in maths. It's just how we guide our learners to having a facility in using them. Visual images can play a positive role in achieving that goal.

In the 1970s, Bruner suggested three developmental stages of learning – concrete, pictorial and abstract/symbolic – and that teachers should use these stages to scaffold the learning. I shall give some examples of scaffolding when I talk about base-ten materials later in this chapter.

The symbolic stage develops around 7 years old, the age at which (teachers tell me) many children give up on maths. At this stage, knowledge is stored primarily as words or mathematical symbols. The potential advantage is that symbols are flexible. They can be manipulated, ordered and classified, so the user is not inhibited by images that have a fixed relation to the idea they represent.

That 'nothing new' is currently evident in the UK, where we have 'Maths Mastery', a style of maths teaching inspired by teaching techniques in Shanghai. The approach is described as guiding children through three different stages of learning (concrete, pictorial and abstract) as their knowledge and understanding increase. We, in the learning difficulties field, have been doing this for many years. Not as a pedagogical option but as a necessity. I think it's a prime example of learning from the outliers, and in this book, I am advocating employing it across the learning spectrum.

Maths apparatus: Initial thoughts

The 'Nothing new under the sun' applies to maths all too often. For example, that very highly regarded Cockcroft Report, *Mathematics Counts* (1982), talked about maths equipment.

> About ten to fifteen years ago, some of those engaged in mathematical education were advocating the provision of a 'mathematics laboratory' in each secondary school. However, we believe it has become clear that the provision of a single specially equipped room of this kind does not meet the need satisfactorily.

That may be a tad harsh. I think an 'apparatus room' that is easily accessible to all who teach maths in a school is good.

Or the maths toolbox. It should be in every maths classroom. It would contain calcu-lators, compasses, set squares as well as Cuisenaire rods, bead strings, Dienes blocks, counters and such (Figure 11.1).

Figure 11.1 The maths toolbox.

I like to have maths kit to hand when I'm teaching or diagnosing. A toolbox is pretty good for this. When I had my own teaching base in my school, I had my 'Maths Lab'. Well, in truth, it was a small side room with lots of maths stuff inside. And I let, even encouraged, other teachers access it.

I found that different apparatus worked for different ideas I was trying to teach or even with the components that made up the idea. And, of course, different students. This meant I needed a range of stuff – on hand. I always felt that my lesson plans were a good example of an estimation but a responsive one.

Above all my (to me) sophisticated selections of apparatus, built around what was in my head, I had to think like my learners and what was in their heads. Did what I was demonstrating work for them? Hattie said, 'It matters when teachers see learning through the lens of the student'.

Here is one little example. I was showing a group of 11-year-old pupils a 1000 base-ten cube and letting them handle the cube. Owing to my ever-smaller budget, I had bought plastic blocks. Their other advantage was that they were coloured, so I could refer to, for example, 'the red one-thousand cube'. The disadvantage of this 'hollow' cube, as one of my pupils told me, was the weight. 'This doesn't feel like a thousand', he said as he weighed it in his hand. It didn't. So it failed as an illustration of one thousand for him and I had failed to demonstrate the value of one thousand. The budget had to stretch to solid, wooden cubes. It didn't stretch to a million cube (1 m^3).

Of course, apparatus should support your communication of a concept in a way that your pupils understand. Maybe ask them questions such as 'What do you see? What does this show you?' Be prepared to be disappointed, or challenged, with some of their responses.

Some useful kit (not exhaustive) and examples of their use

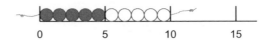

Figure 11.2 Bead strings (with number line).

0–10 bead strings are good for the conservation of 10 when teaching number bonds for 10. The numbers involved may change, say 6 + 4 and 2 + 8, but no bead gets to leave and no bead gets to join the string. I like the string to have 5 white and 5 red beads to keep the key role of 5 in learners' minds.

1–100 bead strings are good for demonstrations such as counting on, and back, in tens, sometimes starting with a number other than 0. Reversing a sequence is an important maths skill. Generalising the place value implications of the digits in numbers is a key skill.

Bead strings are great for the commutative property of addition. As ever, match the pertinent symbols, the digits, to the images.

Cuisenaire rods

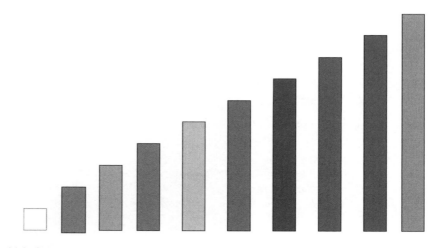

Figure 11.3 Cuisenaire rods.

First created in the 1930s by Cuisenaire and now used as part of Numicon apparatus, these are sophisticated kit and useful beyond basic arithmetic. There are no gradation marks on Cuisenaire rods. Pupils can't use counting to find their value. It's a judgement call based on comparative evaluations. The rods are useful for demonstrating relative values by allowing flexibility in assigning values to the rods. Numicon provides holders with gradations for the rods to slot into in order to circumvent this 'unknown' property if necessary, making grasshopper apparatus into inchworm apparatus. Flexible cognition.

So the basic rod, a white cube, could be 1 or 0.1 or 10 or whatever a teacher chooses for a particular purpose. The other rods have values relative to that choice. The basic rod could be used for algebra and given a value of y, making the next rod 2y, so they can be used for generalising, one of the key skills in maths.

Figure 11.4 shows the rods being used to link multiplication to repeated addition.

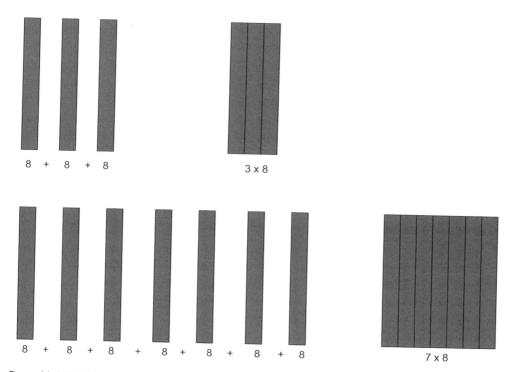

Figure 11.4 Multiplication as repeated addition and the area model.

Figure 11.5 shows the rods being used to present 7×6 as $5 \times 6 + 2 \times 6$, an example of partial products and an example of representing a product as an area. The algebra and generalising development from this example is $7y = 5y + 2y$. This makes for the extension to other examples, such as $7 \times 8 = 5 \times 8 + 2 \times 8$.

The rods show the link between $y = ab$ and area.

Cuisenaire rods are great for 'What else are you teaching?'

Empty, full and sloping number lines

I like number lines because they give a linear image for numbers and help with a broader development of number sense (Figure 11.6). I also like empty number lines. They have a similarity to Cuisenaire rods in that there are no gradations. Again, they can help in taking the learners away from a dependence on counting and maybe encourage them to

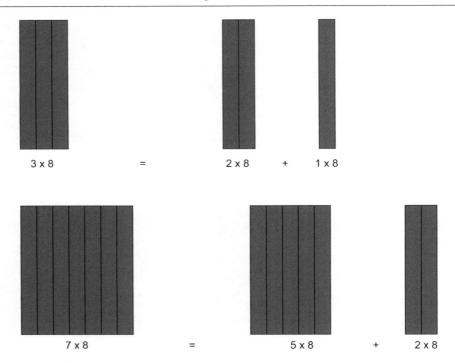

Figure 11.5 Multiplication facts: partial products.

estimate. The 'What else are you teaching?' here is the cognitive skills of the grasshopper. Metacognition rules! Once again, 'Is it bigger or smaller?'

Figure 11.6 Number lines.

I like the sloping number line for rounding up and down (Figure 11.7). You could even modify the 5 with an arrow to show the rule for rounding 5. It is an arbitrary rule and sometimes we need help to deal with arbitrary things.

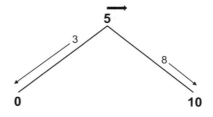

Figure 11.7 The sloping number line.

One of my first special students was as sharp as a tack. I was teaching rounding and had not explained the 5 rule. I asked this student to round 65 to the nearest ten, thinking I might puzzle him. (We had a good classroom ethos so I could do such things without threatening self-esteem.) Not so. He asked me, 'Are you buying or selling?' It's always good to ask your pupils questions, but you've got to be ready for some great answers. Thanks, Benny!

Of course, number lines, and bead strings, provide linear, proportional, one-dimensional images of number.

Base-ten Dienes blocks

Figure 11.8 Base-ten blocks. 1000. 100. 10. 1.

Sometimes research discovers the obvious, but then sometimes the obvious needs to be stated. Apparently, recent studies have pointed out that it may not be helpful to young children if a teacher does not understand the mathematical meaning of base-ten blocks. I like the cautious 'may not be helpful'. Are our young teachers not being shown this stuff in their training? Dyslexia is yet to appear as a significant component in initial teaching training, so not much hope for dyscalculia and maths learning difficulties.

Let's get my opinion up front. Since our number system is a base-ten system, base-ten blocks should be an integral part of maths teaching. That sounds almost logical.

My experience is that one of the trickiest parts of the base-ten system is zero. When I was trialling items for my standardised test (*More Trouble with Maths*), if I wanted to create errors in the computation items and thus get a good distribution of correct/incorrect answers, then slipping in a zero would do the trick. Roman numerals didn't have a symbol for zero. That didn't stop the Romans from ruling the world and they didn't have General Certificate of Secondary Education (GCSE) maths exams.

When we count forwards, we start at 1. When we count backwards, we end at 0. I have mentioned apparent inconsistencies in maths several times in this book. In my Maths Explained tutorial on counting, I start at 0. This is a tricky visual image, though. Maybe you should show something being there to compare with nothing being there?

As my introductory paragraph says, you need to understand and be familiar with the base-ten blocks to use them successfully. And, of course, so do your students. They need to be intuitively familiar with the values and relative values of the blocks.

Figures 11.9 to 11.15 illustrate their use to give visual images of numbers. The numbers can, of course, also be modelled with the actual blocks. I have shown in the series how the scaffolding is removed but that at each stage the digits are on show. This is using Bruner's progression but with the final stage on show throughout (that is, the symbols on their own). It was Bruner who coined the term 'scaffolding' for this procedure. I have slipped in a zero example to show how it is used as a place value holder and how to rename a number ready

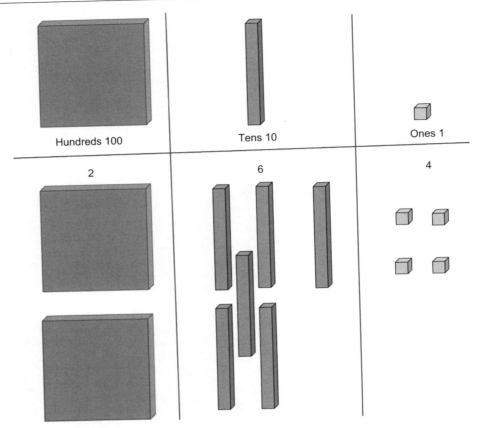

Figure 11.9 Scaffolding. Place value columns, with base-ten blocks, number names and symbols. Number (264) shown with base-ten blocks and symbols.

for subtraction. As ever, encourage metacognition and ask your students what they see and what they think. Challenge them appropriately. Avoid being patronising (See Chapter 5).

Once again, there are Maths Explained tutorials showing the use of visual images of the base-ten blocks for the operations.

Fingers and tallies

Fingers are part of the early stages of understanding number. They are the reason behind our base-ten number system. But we should want to wean children off an over-reliance on counting on their fingers.

When I do lectures for teachers, I often set them a two-part problem: 'What day is it today? So what day was it five days ago?' In this unfamiliar, less practised task, many revert to finger counting. It's quick in this case, so no big deal, but it does illustrate again the power of first learning experiences on future learning.

I really worry in a diagnosis if the child, or sometimes an adult, uses lots of ungrouped tallies or counts a number of objects without grouping them. Maths is very much about grouping and moving away from a reliance on ones.

Number shown with base ten blocks and symbols

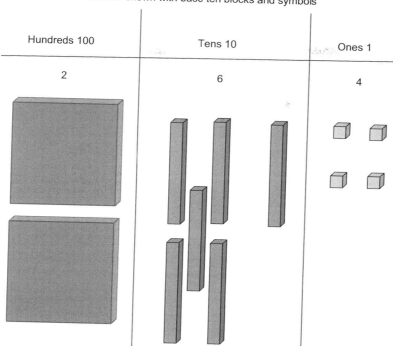

Hundreds 100	Tens 10	Ones 1
2	6	4

Figure 11.10 Place value columns without base-ten blocks but with number names and symbols.

Hundreds 100	Tens 10	Ones 1
2	6	4

Figure 11.11 Place value columns, near names and symbols.

264

Figure 11.12 Number shown only with symbols.

I may have said before, probably several times by now, 'Nothing works for everyone'. It's one reason why we need a collection, a range of maths kit. Here's an example for fingers and the 9x table facts and 'Nothing works for everyone'.

The strategy is to hold up ten fingers. Say you want to know the answer for 4 × 9. You fold down the fourth finger and then count the fingers to the left, 3, and the fingers to the right, 6. Answer for 4 × 9 is 36. This is tricky with 12 × 9. Back to 4 × 9. Some students cannot hold down that fourth finger when they start counting the upright fingers, so the method falls apart.

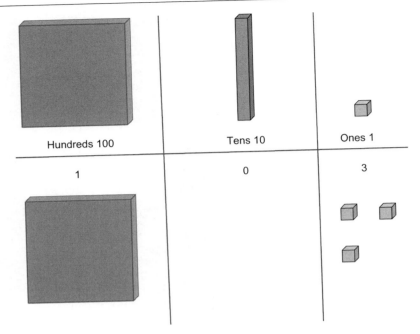

Figure 11.13 Place value columns, base-ten blocks, number names and symbols.

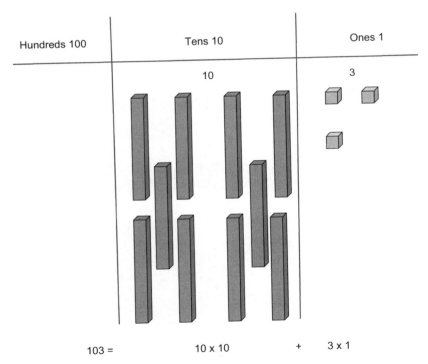

Figure 11.14 Place value columns, number names and symbols. Renamed (first stage) number shown with base-ten blocks and symbols.

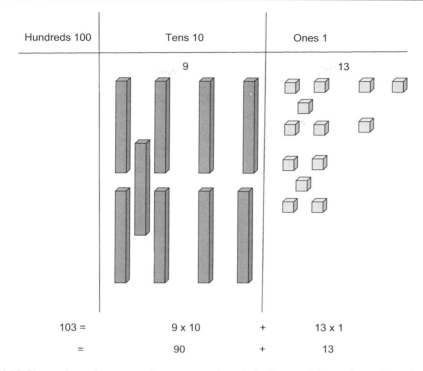

Hundreds 100	Tens 10	Ones 1

9

13

103 =	9 x 10	+	13 x 1
=	90	+	13

Figure 11.15 Place value columns, number names and symbols. Renamed (second stage) number shown with base-ten blocks and symbols.

The goal is to wean the learner off using fingers and an over-reliance on counting in ones. Fingers are my least favourite manipulative. By far. They don't support the development of maths skills and concepts.

Incidentally, that Cockcroft Report (1982), famous but under-implemented in the UK, was titled *Mathematics Counts*. I don't think that was meant to be ironic.

The balance

The balance is good for equals, for basic facts, for equations, for doing the same to both sides of an equation and for demonstrating basic algebra (Figures 11.16 to 11.19c).

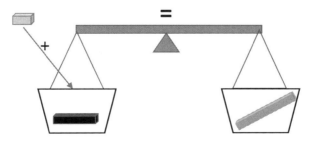

Figure 11.16 Basic fact. A 3 rod added to a 7 rod balances a 10 rod. 3 + 7 = 10.

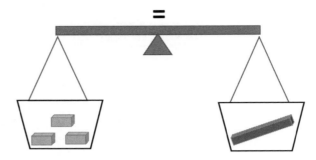

Figure 11.17 Basic fact. 3 × 3 rods = one 9 rod. 3 × 3 = 9. (3 + 3 + 3 = 9).

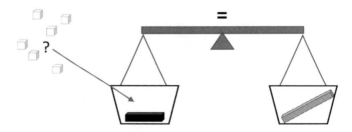

Figure 11.18 What do I add to 7 to make 10? 7 + ? = 10.

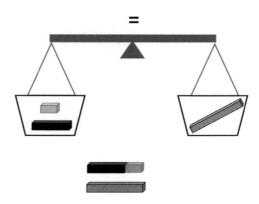

Figure 11.19a 7 + y = 10;   7 + y − 7 = 10 − 7.

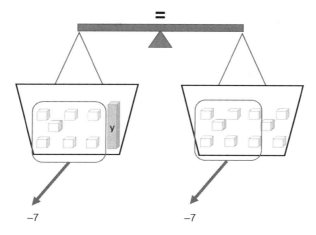

Figure 11.19b $7 + y - 7 = 10 - 7$.

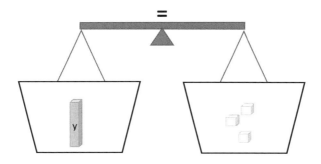

Figure 11.19c $y = 3$.

The sequence of figures should illustrate how algebra develops from number and thus the need to understand numbers and operations.

Doing the same to both sides of an equation and demonstrating basic algebra.

In each of these examples, the maths talk (and symbols) matches the manipulatives and what is being done with them.

Final thoughts

Symbols are abstract and so dealing with them involves memories (that is, short-term memory, working memory and often lots of long-term memory). Visual images and concrete materials can support the learner's memory and strengthen the learning as they link them to the symbols and other facts and concepts and thus to recall and comprehension. They can give a security to a fact or a formula/algorithm.

This chapter is not meant to be an exhaustive list of materials and visual images. It is about encouraging teachers to be creative in finding ways to communicate concepts. And I do like KISS ('Keep it simple, stupid') when making choices of kit. Don't confuse learners with over-elaborate kit or visuals. And keep in mind the age of your learners.

It's good to have a sense, an understanding of 'Why is this so?' That applies to teachers and pupils.

I've dedicated the next chapter to two more visual methods.

Chapter 12

Two visual methods

This chapter looks at two of the most challenging topics in early maths. The approach described includes using paper strips or equivalent visuals (that is, using a paper and/or an area model for fractions and the Singapore bar model method for word problems).

Fractions

What is a fraction? Is this an existential question? I'm not sure, but I know that fractions exist once you're seven years old.

An introduction

Fractions can be puzzling, seemingly illogical, inconsistent and challenging to the patterns that have been learned previously. They come with a bad reputation. Once again, symbols, or their absence, can confuse our learners. Understanding fractions will become easier if the symbols, how they are used and how they relate to the vocabulary, are understood by students. Fractions are on the upward trajectory of the development of maths knowledge and skills, which means there are some foundations that need to be in place. Also, as I said earlier in this book (Chapter 10), there are some deceptive inconsistencies to deal with as well. My argument is that visual images and materials used alongside symbols are needed to secure an understanding of fractions, an argument I made in my first book on dyslexia and maths back in 1993 (*Mathematics for Dyslexics*) and put into practice in my teaching. It's progression à la Bruner; that is, the goal is to get to using just the symbols via the images.

What are fractions? The big picture (of a small part)

The fractions from everyday life are pretty much restricted to half, third and quarter. Even with these, half dominates. I see sale signs in shops saying, 'Half price'. I don't see 'A quarter off'. Certainly, I don't see 5/7 used to describe a five-day working week or a discount in a shop.

   As a starting point, students need to know that a fraction is a part of something. For example, one half of an hour (60 minutes) is 30 minutes, two thirds of an hour are 40 minutes, three quarters of a kilometre (1000 metres) are 750 metres. Even here, we need to be careful with what we might imply. I worked with a 17-year-old who was absolutely convinced that fractions couldn't have a value greater than 1. He had restricted his focus to 'part of' being smaller than one.

To get to a part of something, you must divide. So where is the symbol for divide in:

$$\frac{1}{2} \quad \frac{2}{3} \quad \text{and} \quad \frac{3}{4} \quad ?$$

Fractions hide the divide sign. Maybe that's good for a lot of learners since so many of them don't like division either. But that's just avoidance. The division symbol is there. It's just not all there.

You could visualise the digits 2 and 3 in $\frac{2}{3}$ as covering up the two dots in the divide symbol.

The inclusion of division makes the understanding of fractions harder. Division is often perceived of as the most difficult operation of the four. Fractions are a new application of that concept for the learner. At a basic level, the learner needs to make a (maybe counterintuitive) link of 'more' to 'smaller'. The *more* parts there are in a fraction, the *smaller* each part is. Inverse relationships can be challenging. Cutting up (that is, 'dividing') paper squares into fractions in order to clarify this should be there at the beginning. There are some simple visuals that do this in my Maths Explained videos.

The relative sizes or values of fractions can confuse. They can challenge previous knowledge, so in the series of fractions below, the value of the fractions is getting smaller even though the lower/bottom number is getting bigger. 'More parts' means 'smaller parts'.

$$\frac{1}{2} \quad \frac{1}{3} \quad \frac{1}{4} \quad \frac{1}{5} \quad \frac{1}{6} \quad \frac{1}{7} \quad \frac{1}{8} \quad \frac{1}{9}$$

After an extensive and well-funded research project in the US on children learning fractions, Seigler and his team (*Scientific American*, 28 Nov. 2017) made several very pertinent observations. One of these is particularly relevant here: 'Addressing inherent sources of difficulty in fraction arithmetic, and in particular, an understanding of fraction magnitudes, can also make a large difference'. (I like the use of 'large difference'. It's very pertinent to fraction sizes). They suggested that if learners can place fractions correctly on a number line, then that will demonstrate an understanding of relative values.

How can this be demonstrated?

Back in 1993, when the first edition of our (Chinn and Ashcroft) *Dyslexia and Maths Difficulties: A Teaching Handbook* was published, we showed the use of paper strips and squares to demonstrate fractions and operations with fractions. This next section shows how this idea has been refined. On reading my draft of this chapter, I realised that some of my explanations sounded a tad like a cooking recipe. Does that make it multi-disciplinary? Anyway, it's different in that you need to understand the ingredients.

I talked about number lines in Chapter 11. Here, I need a decimal number line from 0 to 1.0 (Figure 12.1).

Figure 12.1 Number line for 0 to 1.0.

We quartered the thirds and thirded the quarters!

$$\frac{8}{12} + \frac{3}{12} = \frac{11}{12}$$

In words: Eight twelfths plus three twelfths make eleven twelfths.

By the way, I think it was Gattengo who pointed out in a talk that in the middle of 'denominator' is the French word for name, *nom*. A de**nom**inator is the name of the fraction.

It's often good to use words, visual images and symbols together to build an under-standing of a concept. Look at this introduction to division by fractions as an attempt to underpin 'Turn upside down and multiply' (TUDAM) with some understanding. I've been teaching for long enough to know that TUDAM will be the modus operandi in the reality of homework and tests, but it would be good if I had at least tried to explain it.

Let's work through 'division by fractions'. Keep the 'Is it bigger or smaller?' question in your mind and in your students' minds.

Use Figure 12.7a to discuss how many fifths are in 1. The phrase 'How many fifths in 1?' is a verbal version of symbols $1 \div 1/5$. Note that they are in the reverse order to the words. Part of the discussion should include that in this 'fraction smaller than one' situ-ation a division results in a bigger answer. That's the first (apparent) inconsistency dealt with.

$$1 \div 1/5 = 1 \times 5 = 5$$

Use Figure 12.7b to discuss 'How many two fifths in 1?' and that it should be half as many as the number of one fifths. Since 'two fifths' is twice as big as 'one fifth', there will

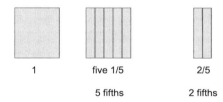

1	five 1/5	2/5
	5 fifths	2 fifths

Figure 12.7a Dividing 1 by 2/5.

1/5

2/5 2/5

Figure 12.7b Dividing 1 by 2/5. How many 2/5 in 1?

be half as many when dividing into 1. So instead of 5, it's 2 ½. That really does have the potential to confuse learners!

$$1 \div \frac{2}{5} = 1 \times \frac{5}{2} = \frac{5}{2} = 2\frac{1}{2}$$

I have found that getting an answer that is another fraction can challenge intuition and that questions such as

$$\frac{7}{8} \div \frac{3}{5} = \frac{7}{8} \times \frac{5}{3} = \frac{35}{24}$$

can give mind-boggling answers. A 'bigger or smaller' appraisal might give some reason to 35/24 and at the same time review basic understanding of fraction values. So, if the learner can realise that 7/8 is bigger than 3/5, 'How many 3/5 in 7/8?' should give an answer that is more than 1 (and less than 2). That first comparison of the relative values of 7/8 and 3/5 might require some folding of paper squares. Using reference values such as ½ and 1 can help when linked with questions such as 'Is this fraction bigger or smaller than a half?'

There are two lots of $\frac{2}{5}$ and half of $\frac{2}{5}$ (which is $\frac{1}{5}$)

= 2.5 (two and a half)

My son always used to ask for the 'biggest half' of the cake or pizza. That's not great grammar. It should be 'bigger'. That's not great maths. Halves have got to be exactly equal. It's tricky to do that with a pizza or a cake (and my son). I never seem to get my fair share of chorizo (pizza) or chocolate buttons (cake).

Earlier in this chapter, I mentioned Bob Seigler's paper in *Scientific American*. Here's another quote from that source:

> Moreover, in a nationally representative sample of 1,000 Algebra 1 teachers in the US, most rated as 'poor' their students' knowledge of fractions and rated fractions as the second greatest impediment to their students mastering algebra (second only to 'word problems').

Enough of fractions. Maybe I'll just mention the irony of 'the simplest form of a fraction'. 'Simplest' is relative.

Word problems next.

Word problems

Research from 2000 on the maths topics that special needs teachers in the US found as 'creating the most difficulty for learners' listed 33 topics. These are the first three:

1. *Has difficulty with word problems.*
2. *Has difficulty with multi-step problems.*
3. *Has difficulty with the language of math.*

Word problems are another source of apparent inconsistencies, or maybe even irrationalities, for learners. In fact, most seem to have little to do with real life. I have long thought that there is a secret breeding programme somewhere in the world for people who write word problems, problems that are designed so the students can't get them right. I do acknowledge that the reputation of word problems sometimes makes this a belief long before learners meet them. The opportunities for inconsistencies and confusions that word problems can create are limitless. That makes them hard to teach and makes it hard for learners to experience meaningful success.

Here's a simple example. Compare these two versions of 8 – 5.

From 8 take away 5. Take 5 away from 8.

The change in order of the numbers, from 8 then 5 to 5 then 8, is enough to confuse some learners. It can confuse them when punching numbers into a calculator:

From 307 take away 228. Take 228 from 307.

And another from a discussion on the radio:

'It's more than a half or at least a half'. Do the two versions say the same thing? This is a good discussion for the class.

Here's a question I found on the web. It is an example of bringing 'real life' situations into maths.

Matthew is afraid that his house might catch fire and the money he has saved would burn, so he keeps his cash in a block of ice in a freezer. He has $4024 of frozen assets. Matthew's brother, Kevin, keeps his savings stuffed in a cuddly toy penguin. If Matthew has twice as much saved as Kevin, how much does Kevin have?

That's a lot of words for 4024 ÷ 2, but I like the quirky content. It's a shame about the toy penguin in the fire. And the money.

One of the most mathematically handicapped students I ever assessed was a 15-year-old girl with severe speech and language difficulties. This had a huge impact on her ability to solve word problems but also had a major impact on all areas of her maths.

I thought I'd slip in a couple of examples before I get to the Singapore bar model method. I think they tell us something about how learners interpret word problems when they are not in the 'right' maths mindset. And, Polya, way back in 1957, said that children have an indifference to artificial problems. I guess some word problem writers are slow learners when learning about learners.

I can't remember where I got this from, but it does show a lack of understanding of the size of cakes and ovens or maybe Bill's ability to think (even slightly) laterally:

Bill baked 15 cupcakes in an hour. How many cupcakes could he bake in 4 hours?

The 12-year-old who answered this next one needed more information about these 32 people or indeed whether *every* car could take 5 people.

| A car can seat 5 people. | Yes |
| How many cars do you need to take a group of 32 people to a concert? | 32 |

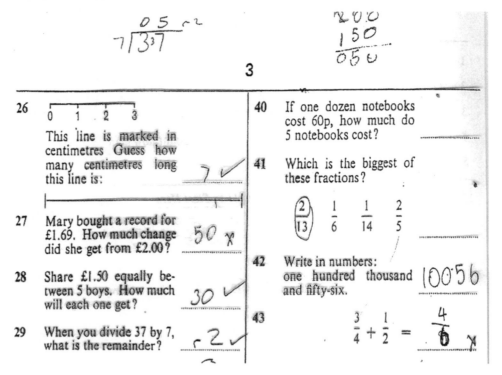

Figure 12.8 Can you spot where the error for question 27 came from?

On a contrary day, I could defend that answer. Maybe on any day (Figure 12.8).

And here is some data from South Africa, end of grade 3, as an illustration of the impact of words on an addition question.

Only half could add 8 to 34 when presented as,

$$34 + 8 = \square$$

This dropped to a quarter when presented as,

"My mother is 34 years old. My father is 8 years older. How old is my father?"

The Singapore bar model method

I should point out that this model came from the mainstream environment. I include it because I like it, but it does show that what is good practice usually works for a spectrum of learners.

I want to focus now on the Singapore model method (Kho Tek Hong et al., 2009) for learning mathematics and how this can guide students as they try to solve word problems, but first I'll briefly mention the range of words used for the four operations because, for some, choice can be confusing. And that's before we get to how they are used in word problems.

+	Addition, add, sum, plus, increase, total, more
−	Subtraction, subtract, minus, less, difference, decrease, take away, deduct
×	Multiplication, multiply, product, by, times, lots of, of
÷	Division, divide, quotient, goes into, how many …. in?

(How about 'How many cars go into a tunnel?')

The Singapore model method and the four operations

This is about giving students a generic approach to problem solving. I've illustrated this using simple examples to encourage engagement.

As I work through some illustrative examples, I think the influence of Bruner's stages of representation is apparent. As a reminder, these are:

Enactive. Representation through actions.
Iconic. Representation through visual images.
Symbolic. Representation through words and symbols.

Basic Example 12.1. Kay had 9 rubber ducks. If she gave away 3 to Jo, how many does she have now?

The question has simple vocabulary. Digits are used for the numbers, so they are easy to identify. However, it has 'gave away' instead of 'take away'. If this was misunderstood, then there may be concern about the student using literal interpretations.

Enactive: Set out 9 rubber ducks (Figure 12.9). Notice that I have used the 5 + 4 arrangement.

Model the problem. $9 - 3 = 6$

Discuss the vocabulary and what it is telling us to do. Look at the other words/phrases for the − symbol and discuss which words could be used instead.

Look at the patterns for the ducks with 9 as 5 + 4 and 6 as 5 + 1. Does this reduce the reliance on finger counting?

Iconic/symbolic: Now draw a bar model in ones (Figure 12.10) with symbols included and use a similar discussion.
Iconic/symbolic: Draw a continuous bar model (Figure 12.11) with symbols included, but no gradations, and use a similar discussion. This could be modelled with Cuisenaire rods.
This approach to this simple example is very much about 'What else are you teaching?'

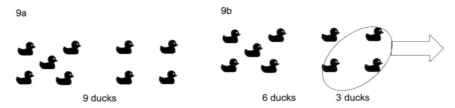

Figure 12.9 (a and b) The rubber duck problem.

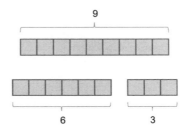

Figure 12.10 A bar model (discrete).

Figure 12.11 Bar model without gradations. (Compare with Cuisenaire rods.)

Basic Example 12.2. Mic had seven more running medals than Sami. If Mic has ten medals, how many does Sami have?

Again, the vocabulary is basic, but now words are used for numbers, so they are harder to spot. One reason for me using this example is that if the word list for symbols is used, then 'more' means 'add'. So a simple analysis by circling the numbers and the operation word is not going to work. The pupils need to get the context, which is where the bar model comes in. In this example, I'm going straight to the ionic/symbolic stages.

First model based on 'Mic has more medals than Sami' (Figure 12.12).

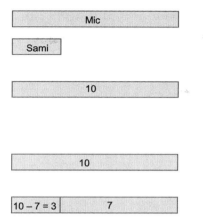

Figure 12.12 Mic and Sami's running medals.

Example 12.3. Oscar trains each week by running 11 km. Jac runs 4 times as far each week. How far does Jac run?

Set up the bars to match the data (Figure 12.13).
    The overview is that Jac runs 4x more:

    Jac   ?

The bars for Jac show he runs 4 × 11 km = 44 km.

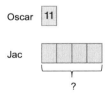

Figure 12.13 Oscar and Jac's weekly runs.

Example 12.4. Oscar runs 8 km each week and Jac runs 48 km. How many times as far does Jac run than Oscar?

Set up the bars, but we don't yet know how many boxes we need for Jac, hence the ~ (Figure 12.14).

There are two routes to the answer.

$48 \div 8 = 6$

How many 8s in 48?

and $8 \times ? = 48 ? = 6$.

What do I multiply 8 by to get 48?

An inchworm solution (see Chapter 7) to 'How many 8s in 48?' would be to use repeated addition of 8. This could lead to some good discussion about multiplication as repeated addition, about making the solution process more efficient maybe by using key multiples 1x and 5x, and the link between multiplication and division.

Although the focus is in solving a word problem, there is scope again for 'What else are you teaching?' Here, that will include encouraging flexibility in the use of operations to solve problems (Figure 12.15).

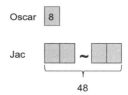

Figure 12.14 Oscar and Jac's weekly runs.

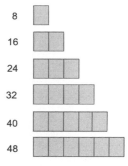

Figure 12.15 Repeated addition of 8.

Example 12.5. Dan collected a total of 120 football cards. He collected 5 times as many Premier League cards as he did from the other Leagues. How many Premier League cards are in his collection?

Set up two bars. One for the 'other' Leagues and one (5 × bigger) for the Premier League (Figure 12.16).

Combine the bars to show that (Figure 12.17).

The number of Premier cards in $5 \times 20 = 100$.

This method is analytical and has visual support at each stage. It should also deal with that infamous instruction, 'Show your working'.

Figure 12.16 The football cards question. Step 1.   *Figure 12.17* The football cards question. Step 2.

Example 12.6. A two-step problem

Dan and Kev share $350 between them in the ratio of 3:2.

How much does Dan get? How much does Kev get?

Dan then gives some of his money to Kev so they both have the same amount. How much does Dan give to Kev? (Figure 12.18)

Set up the $350 bar.

Set up the 3:2 bar.

This shows that there are five 'parts'.

One part is $350 \div 5 = \$70$.

Dan gets $3 \times \$70 = \$210$.

Kev gets $2 \times \$70 = \$140$.

To get the same amount, they must both have $350 \div 2 = \$175$ (Figure 12.19).

$175 = \$210 - \$35$ and $\$140 + \$35$

Dan gives Kev $35.

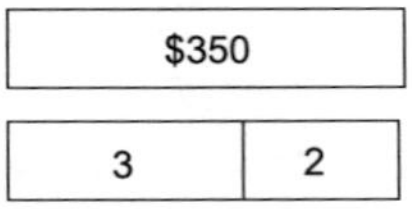

$350

3	2

Figure 12.18 Sharing 3:2.

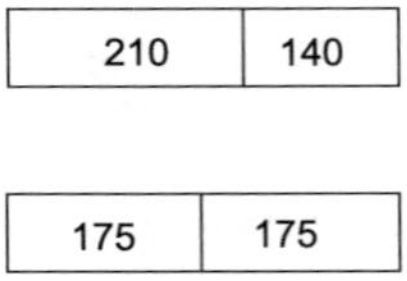

210	140

175	175

Figure 12.19 Equal shares.

Last comments

As a final comment, I would say that the ability to solve problems is one of the most important skills we teach in maths. One of my beliefs is in the transferability of this skill to life as another way, a maths way, of looking at and analysing things. Every subject teaches us different ways to think if we teach them cognitively. That's a bigger goal than rote learning the seven times table facts.

Footnote

Look out for influential little words such as 'not'.

Here is more good advice from Professor Mahesh Sharma. He recommends using reverse translations (that is, converting a number sentence into a word problem). This can be a lot of creative fun. Maybe it will help find future creators of word problems.

Chapter 13

Anxiety and withdrawal

My hypothesis that 'what works for the outliers can be used with other pupils' applies to maths anxiety, too. In fact, I will provide some evidence that maths anxiety is by no means an experience that is limited to low achievers.

When I was first faced with a class of pupils all of whom found it difficult to learn maths, my focus was on cognitive intervention. Later, as I and the other teachers in my school started to see improvements in academic performance, it became apparent that there were many affective issues that had been almost subsumed by cognitive issues. We had been caring. We provided a good environment (R. Burden, 2005), but we needed to be more proactive in addressing self-concept, self-esteem, self-efficacy and motivation and preparing our students to be as independent as possible when they left us to return to mainstream schools.

As with cognitive issues, we found that the problems in the affective domain were not, by any means, unique to our students. And it is still an issue. The 2019 Programme for International Student Assessment (PISA) Report noted that the UK had some of the lowest scores of any country for 'life satisfaction' and for feeling they had 'meaning' in their lives. In England, 66% of young people – compared with an Organisation for Economic Co-operation and Development (OECD) average of 50% – said they were sometimes or always worried. More than those of many other countries, schools in the UK had a strong culture of individual competition rather than co-operation.

Back to my school. As we developed a greater understanding of the potential barriers to learning, we began to introduce classroom management strategies to address some of the concerns (see Chapter 15). Of course, these problems were not new or unique to us. In 1964, John Holt's book *How Children Fail* was a revelation for me. Among his many perceptive observations, many of which are still pertinent today, was this: 'When we give children long lists of arithmetic problems to do, hoping to create confidence, security, certainty, we usually do quite the opposite, create boredom, anxiety, less and less sharpness of attention and so, more and more mistakes and so, more and more fear of making mistakes'. The fear of negative evaluation in maths has drawn more attention from researchers lately (for example, David Sheffield and Tom Hunt from the University of Derby).

Denes Szucs and colleagues' recent report, published by the Centre for Neuroscience in Education at the University of Cambridge (2019), explores the nature and resolution of 'mathematics anxiety' in a sample of 2700 pupils from Italy and England. Of the many interesting and relevant findings was one that referred to parental influence. Primary-age children referred to instances where they had been confused by different teaching methods, including those used by their parents. As I say elsewhere in this book (Chapter 1), every time the curriculum changes there is the risk of disempowering parents. Szucs and colleagues also found that secondary students indicated that the transition from primary to secondary school had been a cause of maths anxiety, as the work seemed harder and they couldn't cope. In the standardised data for my 15-minute maths test in *More Trouble with Maths*, there is a dip in scores for this transition age.

Szucs and colleagues found that there was a general sense that maths was hard compared with other subjects, which led to a loss of confidence. They pointed out that this is not just a low achievers' problem but that high levels of maths anxiety are normal to high achievers in the subject. With higher expectations, there is a higher risk of not coping with failure. They found that the key triggers for anxiety included poor marks, test pressures, teasing by fellow pupils and a confusing mix of teaching methods. The transition to secondary school was challenging. Those classrooms often have a culture and atmosphere that are very different from those of primary classrooms.

Research from Amy Devine (2018) also showed that it is not only children with low maths ability who experience maths anxiety. She found that more than three quarters (77%) of children with high maths anxiety were normal to high achievers on curriculum maths tests. Devine warned that 'because these children perform well at tests, their maths anxiety is at high risk of going unnoticed by their teachers and parents, who may only look at performance, but not at emotional factors'.

I'll just slip in one problem that can be easily addressed. It's that Holt quote again, but I talk about this at least a couple of other times in this book. 'Long lists of arithmetic problems' are still out there as is the optimistic belief among some educators that 'Practice makes perfect'. What can be a contradictory outcome is 'Incorrect practice makes learning imperfect'. (See Chapter 3 and first learning experiences.) As ever, it's not necessarily a complete change in pedagogy that is needed, it is informed moderation, preferably based on an understanding of 'how children learn' (the title of Holt's 1967 companion book to *How Children Fail*). You may have noticed by now that I do like to find wisdom from a while ago as well as new ideas even if the 'new' ideas do sometimes re-invent the wheel. If the old and new are complementary, then that's likely to be an affirmation of veracity.

More recently, the famous composer Harrison Birtwistle said (probably not about maths, but then he doesn't specify that it's not), 'And I can tell you one thing – practice does not make perfect. It makes you a bit better' (2019, *The Times*). So there needs to be a trade-off for the extent of the 'bit better' against the time demanded to achieve it. 'Perfect' is a huge expectation.

As to the importance of the affective domain, another one of my heroes, Ingvar Lundberg, (2006) wrote:

> Over and above common cognitive demands and neurological representations and functions, performance in reading and arithmetic is influenced by a number of motivational and emotional factors such as: Need of achievement, task orientation, helplessness, depression, anxiety, self-esteem, self-concept, loneliness, locus of control, goal commitment, psychological adjustment, metacognition and self-regulation.

That's quite a few influences for schools to deal with. It makes you realise there are many skills we expect from our teachers even if they are not always articulated specifically.

There are, once again, many inter-dependent links to consider. It's complicated. But it is important, as O'Connor and Paunonen (2007), quoted by John Hattie, noted:

'Whereas cognitive ability reflects what an individual can do, personality traits reflect what an individual will do'. I love that quote. It's great for education but sometimes very scary in politics.

The many facets of maths anxiety

We may not know exactly what anxiety is but we know it when we have it. There are many definitions, in that education way with definitions, of anxiety. There have been books on maths anxiety, far more than on, for example, geography anxiety or art anxiety. I have selected a few examples of definitions and explanations of anxiety to illustrate different emphases and interpretations.

Let's start with the difference between State Anxiety, which is specific to a distinct situation such as doing maths, and Trait Anxiety, which is an issue all the time. Maths anxiety is an example of State Anxiety. It could run alongside other anxieties but it doesn't have to.

And, now that living brains are becoming more accessible to researchers, and to allay any doubts about the veracity of maths anxiety, Lyons and Beilock (2012), using functional magnetic resonance imaging, found a compelling neurological reason for highly anxious students to avoid maths. The authors found that the prospect of completing a mathematical task was equivalent to anticipating bodily harm.

I like Data and Scarfpin's (1983) two categories of anxiety:

> Mental block anxiety can be triggered by a symbol or a concept that creates a barrier for the person learning maths. (*Think division or fractions.*)
>
> Socio-cultural maths anxiety is a consequence of common beliefs about maths, such as if you cannot learn facts, you will never be any good at maths. (*Think times tables tests.*)

The first highlights the influence of topics in maths (such as division or fractions) on anxiety. The second reflects the influence of curriculum design, parental attitudes, government attitudes and society's attitudes.

I might add another factor to the socio-cultural category. Often Western societies' attitude to maths is that it doesn't really matter whether you can't do maths. Societies can give mixed messages. In this case, society does demand maths qualifications for so many jobs.

Despite this 'maths doesn't matter' attitude, trying to learn it can impact on the individual. Cemen (1987) defined maths anxiety as,

> A state of discomfort which occurs in response to situations involving mathematical tasks which are perceived as threatening to self-esteem.

I'll return to self-esteem later in this chapter.

Trujillo and Hadfield (1999) bring the focus back to the classroom and the home:

> Anxiety is created by negative classroom experiences, lack of support at home combined with an (extra) anxiety towards testing.

There's always testing. At least it seems to be so in the UK. Maybe that lies behind the PISA comment on competition. Maths lends itself to testing. Maybe this is because maths tests are easier to mark than, say, an English essay. It rarely involves a judgement call beyond 'right' or 'wrong'. I am impressed that there are tests of test anxiety.

Australia's ranking in the 2018 PISA maths table dropped significantly. That has created a lot of anxiety in maths educators in Australia.

An indirect confirmation of the reality of maths anxiety comes from the work of Mark Ashcraft, who found that anxiety could have a negative impact on that important factor for success in maths, working memory.

What creates maths anxiety?

In 2009, I had a paper on maths anxiety published in the journal *Dyslexia*. It was based on surveying over 2000 secondary school students – from mainstream and specialist dyslexia schools – on maths anxiety. The data was collected for males, females and dyslexic males. (There were not enough females in the specialist schools to make a viable sample.) I asked the students to rank 20 anxiety-creating items on one of four grades of generating anxiety.

The top-rated anxiety item for all groups was 'Taking an end-of-term examination'. Once again, I found that asking students about their responses to test items often revealed far more information. For example, one 14-year-old rated every item as 'always creates anxiety' except the 'taking an end-of-term maths exam' item, which he rated as 'never causes anxiety'. I asked him why. He explained, 'The key words are "end of term"'. Clever young man. Just not with maths.

After 'taking an end-of-term exam', the top item for males, females and dyslexics, the other items that ranked high for anxiety were the following:

Doing long division questions without a calculator.
Having to take a written maths test.
Having to work out answers to maths questions quickly.
Waiting to hear your score on a maths test.

I knew that doing maths quickly could be stressful (which is why I put that item in my survey). It's something that can be managed in the classroom but less easily in some other circumstances, such as the UK's Multiplication Tables Check (see Chapter 5), where there was a 6-second time limit on items. I do like the way it's called a 'check' instead of a 'test'. This is a subtle attempt to reduce anxiety. It may not work. I used a similar strategy when collecting data from adults for my 15-minute maths test by calling it a 'survey'. You may have guessed by now that I don't really (or is it 'really don't') like this times tables test.

Taking maths tests and exams rates high for causing anxiety. They're tough on learners if they are learning maths in an exam-heavy environment. Schools don't just set tests and exams, they prepare their students, partly because schools are often judged on the exam results their students achieve. That's a lot of exposure to testing and preparing for testing. But how much learning time should be used for this?

Teachers can manage how they give out scores on maths tests to reduce that fear of negative evaluation. Public recitations of results are not a great classroom strategy. It was interesting that this item was rated low in the specialist schools. I put this down to better classroom management of student welfare.

The study gave me further confirmation that long division was not a favourite topic!

One of the completed survey papers was from a 12-year-old girl. She scored all the items in the middle ranks for anxiety, but she wrote at the top of her paper, 'I am so afraid of taking the common-entrance exam'. This is the examination pupils in the UK took prior to applying for entry to independent schools. (It's to be scrapped in 2020.) There can be parental pressure there, even when not overtly so.

Trying to quantify maths anxiety is not easy. Obviously, it is subjective. However, I work on the principle that it's realistic to make comparisons between items from an individual's responses.

It was no surprise to me that any item that was about a test or an exam attracted a high anxiety rating.

The 'no answer'

One behaviour I had not planned to explore in that anxiety study was the 'no answer', the 'no attempt'. This is the behaviour where a student looks at a maths question, decides it's impossible or decides that they will get a wrong answer and doesn't attempt it. Avoidance and withdrawal are human behaviours outside maths, too. There are several implications for teachers and test compilers here, not least the student who gives up at the first 'impossible' question he or she meets and doesn't skim through the rest of the test to find any 'possible' questions.

I did my first classroom study on this manifestation of anxiety in 1995, when I compared the percentages of no attempts between mainstream and special school pupils:

	Dyslexic	Mainstream
$12.3 + 5$	2.5%	0%
$37.6 - 4$	14.0%	2.2%
33×20	15.7%	3.6%
$6040 \div 10$	39.7%	5.8%
2)39	21.5%	2.9%

In 2012, I did a further study (doi:10.1155/2012/396071) based on the data collected from a large sample from the UK for my 15-minute standardised maths test. The table below is one example of this prevalent trait, even in mainstream schools. The no-attempt percentages are way above the 5% estimate for students with dyscalculia and, apart from the 15-year-olds, above the 25% estimated prevalence for students with maths learning difficulties.

$23 \div 1000$			
Age	Sample	Percentage correct	Percentage 'no attempts'
13 y	191	31.4	38.7
14 y	225	42.2	30.2
15 y	220	46.8	23.6
16–19 y	307	46.9	29.3

It's hard to appraise a student's knowledge if she doesn't answer questions. It's a bit like those detective interviews in TV programmes when the accused answers, 'No comment'.

Of course, the no-answer does not provide any evidence of error patterns. But it does avoid negative evaluations.

If the pass mark for the National General Certificate of Secondary Education (GCSE) maths for 16-year-old students in England in 2019 truly was 21%, then I'd love to know the percentage of no-attempts for every question in the examination. Maybe the suitability of each item could then be discussed. The criteria for selecting each item would be interesting, too.

The pass mark for the maths test for trainee nurses is 100%, which makes sense.

In terms of designing tests, I found this example of what not to do when my daughter (with special educational needs) was given that maths test when applying for post-16 education. It's the quantum leap, an example of the 'giving up' scenario I described above.

Q5. Here is a list of telephone numbers of some of your friends. Which number should you use to telephone Ann?

> *Ali   2540*
> *Andy 2554*
> *Ann   2539*
> *Art   2569*

Q6. Your bus fare to and from the town centre is 45p to get there and 45p to get back. How much change will you have left from a £1?

> A. *5p*
> B. *10p*
> C. *15p*
> D. *20p*

This is beyond belief, except it was real for my daughter and the four other students taking the test.

The quantum leap is from question 5, recognising a name and writing down the associated phone number, to the two-step word problem that is question 6. I think this phenomenon is found all too often in collections of maths questions. It is demotivating. It's an involvement stopper. Check for it when setting 'practice' work, homework, exams or tests. It demonstrates a lack of awareness of student behaviours.

Addressing maths anxiety, self-esteem, self-efficacy and self-concept

Earlier in this chapter and elsewhere in this book, I allude to some interventions that address maths anxiety (for example, managing homework tasks and test papers and being positive in the way feedback and marks are given). There is some overlap here with Chapter 15 on classroom management.

When I was head of a specialist school in the US, I introduced the phrase 'unanxious expectations'. It's not correct grammar, I know, but it summed up my attitude and was a key part of the ethos I was trying to create. I had high expectations for my students, but I did not want those expectations to create anxiety. It's an interesting call, balancing what we want and expect from learners.

One of the most influential books on the affective domain for me was, and still is, Martin Seligman's *Learned Optimism* (1990), where he explains 'attributional style'. We used this concept throughout my school but not in a formulaic way. We let it permeate our care systems, both in the classroom and outside. Professor Bob Burden from the University of Exeter carried out an in-depth research project at the school and had the full and willing co-operation of our pupils. What he found and published as *Dyslexia and Self-Concept* (2005) was contrary to his original expectations:

Very little evidence of learned helplessness.

A high degree of self-efficacy.

An internal locus of control.

And a 'Whole school ethos… success oriented … attribution retraining, albeit at an implicit level, underpinned all aspects of the pedagogy'.

I write in detail about attributional style in *The Trouble with Maths* (4th edition), but, at the core of Seligman's theory, there are three perspectives to challenging students' beliefs:

Permanent. The student believes that the situation will never change and that the bad events that happen are permanent. They feel helpless to change them. So we need to find convincing evidence, even if small, to persuade them that this is not true.

Pervasive. The student can believe that, when a bad event happens, 'Nothing ever goes right for me'. We need to persuade them, again with evidence, that this was a one-off event and that it will not influence future events.

Personal. We need to work on persuading the student that failure is not their fault and that we can help. And, again, we need to give evidence to back that up.

This last one is the one that truly bugs me. I just abhor the circumstances and the experiences that have led to a student believing that it's all their fault. Just bad. And sad.

This is not an instant fix, of course, and we as teachers need to provide cumulative evidence that the negative beliefs are not true. It is the evidence that is so important, not just telling them nicely, although that is better than nothing. We need to pre-empt the problems whenever possible. For example, I might say something along the following lines at the start of an introductory lesson on fractions: 'A lot of people think fractions are difficult and they may be right in that not everyone 'gets' them first time. I'm going to try to explain them this week, but I'm planning to explain them again in a couple of weeks. So, let's see if we can make a start!'

It's about getting the classroom ethos and the whole school/college ethos to be appropriate.

In a final affirmation of the success of our intervention for self-esteem, I'm obliged to relate the true story of a Local Educational Authority inspector's comments at the end of his visit to my school. 'Steve', he said, 'your problem is that you give your pupils too much self-esteem'. He had no sense of humour. This was a criticism.

I offer two thoughts on this, maybe in his defence. As we approached GCSE time, I'd say to my students, 'Time to get to that revision' and some would reply, 'I'm alright. No pressure'.

The second thought came from a psychologist friend. 'People with too much self-esteem can become psychotic'. Psychosis may not be my best gift to my alumni but so far it has not materialised.

Final thoughts

Transactional analysis

Re-aligning attributional style requires effective communication skills. Teaching requires good communication skills. Once again, I go back to an idea that emerged a while ago. In 1958, there was Eric Berne's *Transactional Analysis* and then Harris in 1967 with his book with the great title, *I'm OK. You're OK*. In 2001, transactional analysis in schools was addressed in the book, *Improving Behaviour and Raising Self-Esteem in the Classroom*

(Barrow, Bradshaw and Newton). Transactional analysis deals with interactions between two parties and the attitudes they adopt, Parent, Child or Adult. Basically, good transactions occur when there is empathy between each party and they respond appropriately to the other party. That involves what is said, how it is said and the physical attitude and facial expressions of the communicators.

When I look back on my school days, I remember that transactions were inevitably Critical Parent to Passive Child.

Worth checking out this transactional analysis stuff

Keeping the student in a break-times

This is not often a good strategy. It can have affective consequences. Students need breaks.

The lack of a break may well create problems for the person who teaches the next lesson, not the person who took the break away.

Chapter 14

Assessment and diagnosis of mathematical difficulties

One of my first memories of moving from mainstream to special education is that one of my new colleagues had access to all these specialist tests for spelling, reading, memory and more. He wasn't a psychologist. He was a teacher. I had clocked up 14 years of teaching in mainstream and had never met a teacher like this before. This seemed to me to be a 'magic' skill, way beyond setting an end-of-term test for my Year 10 physics class.

I think that there is still some of this mystery hovering around the assessment and diagnosis of performance and behaviours in education today. Wise people advise us on the correct procedures to follow with assessments (for example, the SASC – SpLD Assessment Standards Committee – in the UK and the American Psychiatric Association in the US). I'm now going to attempt to do that, cautiously, but in what I hope is a pragmatic and classroom-based way rather than in a 'I'm a specialist, so there' way.

With 24 years as a head teacher of specialist schools (including one in the US) behind me, I've read many, many educational psychologist reports, some written with an agenda, such as to contribute to a review for funding extra provisions in a school or to justify special accommodation for examinations, and some to answer the worries of a parent about their child's learning, or lack of learning, in school. I've experienced useless tests both in my work and on a personal level with my daughter. For example, when she was about to start at a post-16 college, she and three other potential students were sat down, given a pre-entry maths test paper and told they had an hour to do what they could. I had asked to be present as I figured I knew something about testing at that stage in my career and I was interested in what would be done. An hour later, she had filled in her name. The other three students had attempted two questions each. 'Inappropriate at so many levels' is the kindest judgement I could come up with. A test needs to be useful and user-friendly. It should find out that useful information about learners, not just confirm their (the learners') opinion that they don't know anything about maths (see also Chapter 13). The learner needs be involved in the process. No input, no information.

Assessment and diagnosis

I'm going to be succinct, firstly because this is a big topic and secondly because I have a book, a manual of tests, procedures and guidance, out there and now in its third edition (*More Trouble with Maths: A Complete Manual to Identifying and Diagnosing Mathematical Difficulties and Dyscalculia*).

Many of us use the words 'diagnosis' and 'assessment' interchangeably, but they are different.

Assessment is about measuring a student's achievements, skills and deficits.

Diagnosis is about understanding why a student is not learning or why he or she is under-achieving and it should also lead to advice on how to teach the child.

Basically, 'I want to know what you can and can't do' is assessment whereas 'I want to know why you can or can't do it' is diagnosis.

I believe that teaching and diagnosis should be inextricably linked in the everyday classroom. The National Association of Head Teachers' Commission on Assessment from 2014 stated that 'Those who cannot assess cannot teach'. I'll expand on this later in the chapter.

Dyscalculia

I want to mention dyscalculia here to give an extra perspective on diagnosis. Dyscalculia is a relatively new kid on the special needs block. At this time, only a few people are qualified to diagnose it, partly because there isn't much training out there and partly because the definition is a work in progress. It's hard to diagnose something that isn't defined. In the UK, the SASC published a paper on diagnosis in 2019. This included a definition of dyscalculia and some comprehensive guidelines on diagnosis. That is a big responsibility.

My university years were spent studying science and consequently my concept of definitions is that they are precise. The problem with defining things about people is that there are a tad more variables involved than, for example, with 'acceleration'. That shouldn't stop us trying to create definitions but it's relevant to keep those variations and the human context in mind. I try to inhibit my science-based mindset to adjust to this new discipline. First learning experiences dominate … again.

So, to go some way towards dealing with this, I have usually written and spoken about 'maths learning difficulties and dyscalculia' together. There is a spectrum. There is a normal distribution. I did debate with myself whether or not to put a large illustration of the normal distribution on the front cover of this book as it is involved in so much of what I write about. This spectrum also supports my 'extrapolating up' approach. Maths learning difficulties are there for (at least) 25% of the population.

Here is an example from when I was a head teacher. I tried to get appropriate accommodation for exams for my students. One of the criteria I remember, way back, was that the cut-off from the spelling test was a score equivalent to 10.2 years. Of course, there had to be a cut-off, but it was tough if your spelling age was 10.4 years. Precision in circumstances like this should be open to pragmatic debate. Avoid the 10.4 effect.

In a diagnosis, I try to keep in mind the many, often interacting factors that are influencing what I am trying to measure. I don't want those 10.4 students to miss out completely.

What are you testing?

I'll start with a failure! I struggled, and failed, to come up with a direct test for 'speed of doing maths' for my diagnostic protocol. There are indicators of speed in some of the component tests in my protocol (for example, the basic fact tests and the 15-minute arithmetic test), but the behaviour that gets in the way of any secure measure is the 'no answer'.

Experience from my studies and research, such as collecting data for my 15-minute test, reveals that the 'no answer' is a prevalent occurrence. The student appraises the problem ('It's a fractions question, I don't do fractions') and doesn't try. This makes it hard to produce a level playing field for all learners when measuring speed of working.

The consequences are that I have yet to find maths tests for speed of working that can do this to my satisfaction.

However, during a full assessment, I have enough tests and activities for me to get a good sense of speed of working. I just don't have a standardised measure of this specific learning factor.

I don't like to extrapolate from tests that don't involve the person actually 'doing' maths. That's too uncertain.

Tests for the ability to solve word problems in maths have issues, too. The vocabulary used in any test is the obvious one. It shouldn't be a reading test. It should be testing maths. Trying to clear the irrelevances from any test is a key skill to creating a relevant test.

So look carefully at any test and ask, 'What is this test testing?' and maybe 'What else is this test testing?'

What to assess

It's the nature of this book (well, the nature of maths) that many of the topics overlap. In Chapter 6 on 'Learner characteristics and key skills', I cover most of the factors that would need to be assessed in a diagnosis. Back in 1991 (*Factors to consider when design-ing a test protocol in mathematics for dyslexics. In Snowling, M. and Thomson, M. (eds) Dyslexia: Integrating Theory and Practice*), I suggested that a diagnostic protocol for investigating maths learning difficulties would include the following:

A norm-referenced test
Counting (forwards and backwards)
Number bonds
Multiplication and other basic facts (and compensatory strategies)
Place value
The four operations ($+ - \times \div$)
Language and symbols
Word problems
Cognitive (thinking) style
Anxiety and the affective domain.

I would now add to this subitising, short-term memory and working memory. These are included in my *More Trouble with Maths* protocol.

One of my principles in creating tests is that the test should measure as directly as pos-sible the relevant component of learning. Another principle is that the test should allow the subject, the learner, to perform at their best. For example, I want to reduce the nega-tive impact and influences of anxiety as far as possible. That involves the ambiance of the test situation and the look of the test, how it appears to the person taking it. Being able to communicate empathetically, listening, responding appropriately, and encouraging metacognitive reflections are key to conducting an effective diagnosis.

I do like to focus on my subject when I'm assessing. I have my own copy of each test so that I can efficiently note behaviours such as pauses, finger counting, secure answers and sub-vocalising. Online testing can be OK, but a lot of information is missed.

Factors to consider and address when testing and when setting homework

I'm guessing that you have noticed that some children get anxious about any form or level of maths tests. When I was collecting data for my anxiety 'test', the top item for generating anxiety was 'Taking an end of term maths exam'. I used to give tests to my students, not to exacerbate their anxiety but in the hope that enough exposure and practising would lower anxiety levels. Key to any full assessment I carried out was the first ten or so minutes when I did my best to put the student at ease. I wanted to get the best out of them so that I had a true picture of what they could and couldn't do. I explained each test and told them that sometimes I would increase the difficulty so that I knew their top score and that that might involve them eventually finding an item/task too hard. Or I might say that the test was designed for older students as well; and that way, I might exceed their capacity by, for example, increasing the number of digits in the working memory test until they could no longer retrieve all the digits. I wanted to pre-empt any situation that generated a fear of failure.

An observation based on my physics teaching days is an interpretation of the Heisenberg uncertainty principle or an extrapolation to humans. I'm drawn to any principle that is uncertain. Heisenberg said that it is impossible to know the exact position and the momentum of a particle simultaneously. That is, the more exactly the position is determined, the less is known about the momentum and vice versa. My human version is that when you try to measure someone's behaviour, the act of measuring may change the behaviour. Anxiety is an example of a factor that changes behaviour. The vocabulary in the test would be another, as would working memory and so on. The question to ask yourself is 'Am I sure I am testing what I intend to test?'

Time and speed of processing are issues for many children and students when attempting maths tasks. I remember that, many years ago when I was talking to teachers about allocating extra time for dyslexic students taking tests, one teacher asked, 'What's the big deal? Why don't we give extra time to all students?' It was one of my first experiences of someone suggesting extrapolating up from 'special' to mainstream. When I was in the US, we used to give extra time automatically, but we gave students a different coloured pen to use in the extra time so that we could monitor its impact.

Another example of learning from my students was the design and trials of the basic fact tests for my diagnosis manual, *More Trouble with Maths*. My students usually liked helping with checking out my ideas and giving me feedback, but not this time and not with this test. With their permission, I gave my Year 7 students my first attempt at a format for a test of basic multiplication facts. I thought the design was fine, not exciting but probably functional. I presented them orally with 12 facts, to be answered at a rate of 5 seconds per fact. (Check out the UK Department of Education's new multiplication fact test where 6 seconds are allowed per item.) After around four items, my pupils were distraught. I felt terrible and told them to stop as 'I'd got that wrong'. Time is a critical factor in testing. I redesigned the tests to remove it as a barrier.

What appears in my diagnosis book are four tests for basic facts, one for each operation. Thirty-six items are presented on an A4 sheet, and the students are asked to answer as many as they can in 1 minute each for add and subtract and in 2 minutes each for multiply and divide. (I tell them, 'That's long enough'.) My Year 7s were not at all stressed out by this format and subsequently I have never stressed out a child or adult when using the tests as part of a full diagnosis. This format takes away the time pressure.

If I am working with an individual, I can watch the way they do each example. For instance, I can usually spot the finger-counting strategy or when the test is over I can ask 'How did you work that out?' if I think they are using linking strategies.

By the way, the UK Department of Education is checking multiplication facts up to 12×12 for Year 4 pupils. For people of my age, my joke is 'That's gross'. For younger folk/teachers, I get a blank look. Shows the Government is on the ball.

Linked to this, teachers could consider offering extra time for homework. However, students do not have infinite time in their day, and in a benign world, they might just be allowed some down time.

I think it's especially hard on a learner who spends a long time struggling to do some homework task if the teacher says, 'Is that the best you can do? You need to spend more time on your homework'.

When I do a full assessment for maths, I reckon I have an hour – or maybe 90 minutes with an older and more relaxed student. The consequence of this is the need to be time-efficient without putting pressure on the student to work too quickly for comfort. As an example, one component of my test protocol is a standardised test of basic maths to determine the student's performance in comparison with that of his or her peers. So how long is enough time for the test? I compromised and allocated 15 minutes from my diagnosis time. I should point out again that, during the test, I will be watching the student and have my own copy of the test so that I can note my observations, some of which I'll use to get more information afterwards, using the 'Can you tell me how you did that?' question. That's a way of introducing a formative perspective into a summative situation. Also, some of my test items have been designed to reveal common errors and misconceptions and cognitive style so that I don't always have to ask. I minimised the use of words to circumvent reading issues. So the items were designed to maximise the 'doing maths' information I could glean from the test.

When I marked the tests (2000+) for standardising this 15-minute test, it was notice-able how many 'no attempts' there were. Not surprisingly, this strategy is more common with low achievers. No attempt – no cross – not wrong.

If we regard ongoing teaching as ongoing diagnosis, then some consideration could be given to the diagnostic content and design of class worksheets and homework tasks. Specific criteria can be built into any worksheet or homework to an extent that is appropriate for the situation. I look at some pages in some textbooks and 'Pow!' – just an overwhelming blur of numbers, too many and too close together. I'm not that keen on cartoons either. They're too distracting and they have a tendency to make the page look age-inappropriate for older learners who need to go back to the basics.

Sometimes, for homework sheets, it is worth considering giving out the sheets before the end of a lesson so that students can attempt the first two questions before they leave. If they get those wrong, then the worksheet may not fulfil its purpose. Worse still, the student may practice a wrong procedure and that might create a dominant entry to the brain. How you then manage this situation is probably down to your specific circumstances.

It's also worth looking at a worksheet or exercise and asking yourself, 'How many of these questions do I really need to use?' Think of the slow workers and the normal distribution.

Here is a penultimate thought. The 'What else are you teaching?' question has a sister question, 'What else are you testing?' One question is, when checking procedural skills, whether by test or homework sheet, do the numbers used act as a barrier (for example, knowing 6×7 for the computation, 36×57)? The student may fail because of a number fact rather than not knowing the procedure. It's another example of why it's worth looking for error patterns.

Here is a last thought. How do you feed back the outcome, the results of the test or assessment? Done without appropriate empathy, that could undo all the good the procedure was designed to achieve. In class, the way results of tests are fed back could be another nail in the coffin that is demotivation. For this reason, I do have some concerns about star charts on classroom walls.

Evidence

Extracts from the Educational Endowment Fund/Nuffield publication, (2018) *Improving Maths in Key Stages 2 and 3. Evidence Review.* (Key stages 2 and 3 cover ages 7 to 14.)

Recommendation 1: Use assessment to build on pupils' existing knowledge and understanding.

Exemplary teaching: Careful consideration is given to how the results of an assessment will be used before an appropriate assessment is selected.

Teachers use a variety of types of assessment, as appropriate, to collect information about strengths and weaknesses. They adapt their teaching in response and use the assessment information to inform planning.

Teachers have a good knowledge of the common misconceptions in maths and why they arise. They use this knowledge to inform their assessment.

Teachers use their knowledge of common misconceptions to plan future lessons.

Feedback is effective.

Check out: *More Trouble with Maths: A Complete Manual to Identifying and Diagnosing Mathematical Difficulties and Dyscalculia* (3rd edition, 2020).

The tests and checklists contained in *More Trouble with Maths* (2nd edition, 2017) were approved in 2019 by the SpLD Test Evaluation Committee (PATOSS) for inclusion in both its pre-16 and post-16 '*List of Suitable Tests for the Assessment of Specific Learning Difficulties (SpLD)*'.

Chapter 15

Classroom management

If we want to maximise the effectiveness of communication in our classroom, there are some proactive things we can do. In this chapter, I have made some suggestions, mostly based on awareness of student needs (not surprisingly). Usually, I have explained the reasons behind the suggestion. Communication is more effective when the person we are communicating with is open to receiving and engaging with the communication. We need to consider the affective domain in any communication. And the classroom ethos.

There are many suggestions about things to do for classroom management throughout this book.

Writing

In my daughter's special school, there was always a jar of pencils on the teacher's desk for those (a large percentage of the students) who forgot to bring one. Of course, you've got to set up an effective collecting-back routine. This strategy meant that every child had access to a writing tool. So there was no problem with the first stage for being ready for writing.

For those students who have problems organising their work on the page, you could offer squared paper. It is unlikely that there will be a universally appropriate size of square. You should ensure that this accommodation doesn't single them out as a student with problems. Maybe all students get squared paper for maths? That 'not single out' will apply to most accommodations.

There may be times when you give extra time. Time is not always available, so have sheets with carefully selected fewer examples and maybe sheets with carefully selected extra examples for the high achievers.

In longer tests or examinations, give extra time, maybe after a supervised break. You could change the pen colour for the extra time so that its impact can be seen.

Copying from a board, book or screen may not be quick or accurate, often because of a low-capacity short-term memory. This task requires that the pupil see the information, remember it long enough to write it down, look up/across and find the correct place and repeat the process. Handouts could be good. And technology in schools is changing so much. It would work here.

The design of worksheets, handouts, textbooks and presentations should be considered. Factors such as font size, spacing, illustrations and colour can all affect accessibility. Personally, I'm against clutter and most cartoons.

Some students write very little because of their cognitive style. They process in their head and do not document how they work. This does not match our exam system in the

UK, where we expect them to 'show your working' (as opposed to 'show you're working'.) At Advanced-level maths (18 years old), you will fail if there is no 'working' even if you get every question right. I'm pretty sure you could pass the national General Certificate of Secondary Education (16 years old) getting every answer wrong if you showed your working.

I like wipe-clean boards for class work. Mistakes are not permanent. They give more students access and encouragement towards engaging in tasks.

When I am doing a diagnosis, I have a selection of pens and pencils for the subject to choose from. Inevitably they go for the pencils. Maybe I encourage this by having an eraser there, too.

Computers do corrections so well. (Thank goodness!)

Instructions

My wife has been known to say to me, 'I've told you that three times already'. I remind her that she has not worked in special needs and that 'three' is just a beginning. I understand that behaviours such as mine can be frustrating for others. It can be hard to always notice them in a class. Some students do invisibility (see below). Short-term memory is one of those normal distribution areas. That means there will be a range of short-term memories in every class. Giving out verbal instructions is a skill and one factor in developing that skill is knowing how much to say in each chunk. And what to repeat.

At my 'specialist' school, we had a good reputation for rugby with a team picked from around 25 students across three year groups beating schools with 100+ in a year group. This was due to their motivation, good coaching and appropriate adjustments. For example, in those huddles when a tactic was selected for, say, a line-out, teams had codes for practised routines. Our codes had to be cognisant of short-term memory capacities. They were short.

Short-term memory does not store information. Once the information is forgotten, it is gone. Saying 'Focus, try and remember' is a waste of time and can create anxiety which then will make memory worse.

Some schools use a 'buddy' to help students with such problems. It can be great, but both buddy and pupil need to be happy with the arrangement. When I was working in Singapore, a friend greeted me with the words, 'Bad news, Steve. My son's buddy has just resigned!'

Some students who are not doing well have the skill of becoming invisible. Where they choose to sit in the classroom can help that. Considerate intervention can help both student and teacher. For example, a seat at the back of the class allows a teacher to see and react when the student needs help without the rest of the class seeing. That position allows the teacher to provide intervention more discreetly whilst allowing her to keep an eye on the rest of the class.

Presenting information

It's communication again.

Do you know of your pupils, 'Can they see? Can they hear?' There is far more subtlety to those questions than their three words imply. Here are a couple of examples. I have mentioned (Chapter 10) a pupil I taught who couldn't hear the difference between 'hundred' and 'hundredths', which made decimals a total mystery for him. Asking and listening to his answers alerted me to his problem, which then made it also my problem. And there was the 12-year-old daughter of a former student who brought her to see me for a maths diagnosis. I realised she had vision problems, but she had hidden them from her parents and teachers. Or maybe she hadn't realised she had this problem if she had no 'normal' experience for comparison.

The learning environment is critical. Some classrooms are a wonderland of posters, mobiles (hanging, arty things, not phones), kit and general clutter. Some are blank and boring. Somewhere in between is good. Being age-appropriate is good. Clutter can be very distracting to some students and that can be visual clutter or verbal clutter. Some textbooks and computer programmes suffer from this, too. It may still be the case, but some years ago when I was working in the US, under-graduate students could ask for a 'vanilla environment', a distraction-reduced testing environment for their exams, a shielded bland space, or a carrel desk.

As an aside here, there was a meta-analysis of the effectiveness of digital-based interventions from 15 studies published between 2013 and 2019. The analysis indicated that digital-based interventions 'generally improved mathematical performance though there was a significant heterogeneity across studies'. There was no evidence that video games offered additional advantages with respect to drilling and tutoring approaches. I would be interested to know the impact of the design of the images used on the screen.

When I lecture, I use uncluttered slides and coloured fonts, often alternating the font colour for different points. There is some controversy about the use of colour in reading, but I find that setting up slides in this way is no big deal. It helps people focus on specific areas. It helps address short-term memory problems. It's probably good classroom practice for many students, too.

I remember that in my early years of teaching we had blackboards and chalk. Trendy schools had green boards. Cleaning a board involved lots of chalk dust, so I tried to make a board last a whole lesson and then let the day's blackboard monitor clean it. This resulted in me squeezing bits of information into any odd space I could find and then expecting the pupils to find it and copy it. Ultimately, technology solved the chalk dust problem via the overhead projector. However, retrospective guilt remains. What we can do now with information technology (IT)-based presentations is so very far beyond what I could have predicted back then.

Through my connections with the Centre for Applied Special Technology (Boston, MA, USA), my school was the first in the UK to have voice output and, later, voice recognition. It was expensive (at the time) but worth it. And now there's an iPad per child in some classrooms. Giving out information, and collecting it, has changed so very much since that green board and chalk.

In Chapter 12, I discussed the use of visual images and materials in presenting and explaining concepts and procedures and the relevance of Bruner's work.

Worksheets and homework

Once a student has taken the worksheet home, a teacher has no input or control over what happens when the student attempts the worksheet. Should the practice session result in wrong answers, the student is feeding incorrect information to the brain. I'm back to my interest in old research and to Buswell and Judd (1925), who realised that the first learning experience of a new topic created a dominant entry to the brain and that subsequent attempts to replace the information were likely to be temporary.

The brain has to inhibit the wrong information before the new information can become secure. Then, in 1942, Luchins wrote about *Einstellung*, described as a mental inflexibility that creates a tendency to respond to situations in a certain, fixed way. For example, a person who successfully solves a series of problems using just one formula may apply that same formula to a new problem even if it is not appropriate. Currently, a related phenomenon, 'inhibition', is getting interest from researchers.

Key Finding 1 from the National Research Council book *How People Learn* (2000) also revisits Buswell and Judd's work: 'Students come to the classroom with preconceptions about how the world works. If their initial understanding is not engaged, they may fail to grasp the new concepts and information that they are taught, or they may learn them for the purposes of a test, but then revert to their preconceptions outside the classroom'.

To repeat a point from the previous chapter, how practical would it be in your class to let students attempt the first two questions on a worksheet and then swap and mark with another student before they take it home? If the answers are wrong, what alternatives would you have ready instead of reinforcing incorrect learning with more examples?

I found it useful to ask myself, 'What am I testing or practising with this homework?' If it's not about checking the ability for basic fact recall, then maybe a times tables square could be provided or a basic calculator allowed. For the worksheets in my Maths Explained tutorials, I make extensive use of 1, 2, 5, 10, 20, 50 and so on, so that the focus is on the concept or the procedure and not on the ability for basic fact retrieval.

It's difficult to assess how much time a student has spent on homework tasks. Sometimes what is handed in does not reflect the effort and time that went into producing it. The teacher's reaction to this could contribute to either motivation or demotivation. That, in turn, will contribute to the classroom ethos.

'Is that all you've done?' is to be used only with care and with an understanding of the learner.

Although it will vary from individual pupil to individual pupil, also try to have a couple of warm-up questions first on the worksheet. This is similar to checking whether the first two questions are correct but also realising and acknowledging that exercising the brain can be a tad like exercising the body.

How work is marked can influence motivation and the student's perception of themselves as a learner. This is more subtle than not writing big red crosses on every mistake. Comments can be constructive. Even the marks can be presented constructively. I was looking through the exercise book of a pupil I was interviewing for a place in my school. I noticed that he had answered 13 questions correctly and one incorrectly and the mark given was 13/30. Since I couldn't compute that, I asked the pupil why 13/30? 'There were 30 questions, but it took me ages to answer 14'. A comment from the teacher along the lines of 'Well done so far' might have made a positive contribution to this student's negative attitude to maths.

Sadly, negative comments can be long remembered, often for far longer than the positive ones. I was at a reunion of students from 30-plus years ago and one had brought his school report to show me where I had written a less-than-encouraging comment. Retrospective guilt again. By the time I had set up my school, I had learned to check every report to edit out any such comments.

Working and short-term memories

These two memories are critically important for mental arithmetic. Long-term memory for basic facts and procedures is also a factor. Mental arithmetic is not a good experience for students with poor memories, but these memories are also influential across all areas of maths.

Short-term memory is needed to hold the question for that short term, around 15 seconds, but it also depends on distractions. The first requirement for answering a mental arithmetic question is to remember the question. If the teacher repeats the question, that may help. If the teacher works with a student using something like this, '500 minus 197. 500 minus 197. I'm coming back to you in a minute to get you to do that 500 minus 197 question'. The minute passes. 'OK. How you getting on with that 500 minus 197 question?' (Which gives the student a postponement option.) Or the teacher could show the question, on a white board or screen, whilst saying the question. And maybe do that for all the students so as not to draw attention to the students who really need that intervention. Once again, it's the 'What are you testing?' factor.

Recognition of the role of working memory in maths is relatively recent but not yet universal. One of the maths activities most affected by a poor working memory is mental arithmetic. In this activity, the brain has to process information, usually in steps, on the way to obtaining the answer. Any problems with retrieving basic facts will extend the time and number of steps. This is working memory working or memory being over-worked.

Working memory for a population will be distributed as in the normal distribution. So around 68% of the population will be average and 16% below average, which is a significant number of pupils in every class. Typical adults will have a working memory of around seven items, young children around four items. It's helpful if we know which students in our classes have low working memory capacities and adjust how we work with them accordingly. Another informal survey of teachers at my lectures suggests that quite a fair proportion of teachers these days do know about working memory.

There's an interaction here with cognitive style and another example for encouraging metacognition. Using an inchworm procedure for mental arithmetic problems will usually take more steps than using a grasshopper approach.

A further example, similar to the one in Chapter 7, is the question 520 – 197.

Grasshopper	Inchworm
Estimate. 520 – 200 = 320 Appraise. (Is the answer bigger or smaller than the estimate?) Adjust. 320 + 3 = 323 Two steps with 'simple' computations	Picture in the mind as a written algorithm. 520 − 97 Rename 520 as 510 + 10. Subtract 7 to have 3 in the ones place. Rename 510 as 400 + 110. Subtract 110 − 90 = 20 to have 2 in the tens place. Subtract 400 − 100 = 300 to have 3 in the hundreds place. Retrieve the ones and tens digits from working memory. Reverse order of the digits obtained in the procedure. Combine the digits. 323.

Short-term memory and working memory could fail at any stage in that inchworm procedure. That, and not mathematical knowledge, would be the underlying reason for failing to answer. Maybe it would be worth comparing the mental response with a written response.

There is more bad news. Anxiety will have a negative impact on working memory capacity. So, if the student is anxious about mental arithmetic, they will be even less mentally ready to solve questions. Indeed, if the student is anxious about maths in general, the performance will be handicapped. Thus, it is helpful to reduce anxiety as much as possible in the maths classroom.

Classroom ethos and student well-being (see also Chapter 13)

Whatever current trend or ancient wisdom you follow to build a positive ethos in your classroom, your persona is the dominant factor. It's worth taking a fresh look at transactional analysis such as Eric Berne's (1964) work or Barrow, Bradshaw and Newton's (2001) update for thoughts on communication.

Communication should be a two-way activity. I have learned so much of what I know about teaching from listening to my students. John Holt (*How Children Fail*) said much the same over 50 years ago, 'Most of what I have learned about teaching, I learned from the bad students'.

I'm going to give the rest of this section to comments from students. These are some of the observations listed for me by a group of dyslexic students at a study and activity day I had organised for them. I think the two lists are apposite for all learners.

What hinders learning

Teachers who go too fast and expect too much.

Teachers who do not stick to the point.

Too much copying off the board and/or dictating notes. Rubbing work off the board too soon.

Having test results read out loud.

People who make fun of me or who are sarcastic.

Being told off when I ask a friend for help.

Being made to read aloud in class (*or answer maths questions aloud*).

What helps learning

Help being given discreetly and quietly.

Being given more time.

Handouts with summaries of work.

Marking work in dark colours, tidily.

Praise.

Working in smaller groups.

Trained teachers who care.

Grades that show individual improvement.

Marking that is clear and helpful.

Catch-up exercises.

Chapter 16

Bringing it all together

I thought I'd select some of the key points from each chapter as an overview. You may find other points in this book that are key for you and your situation. I have tried not to tell readers what to do, because I am a great believer, based on experience, that teachers each have their own style. That doesn't mean they can't be forever looking for and meeting those new ideas which continue the development that makes a good teacher.

Chapter 1

The goal of this book is to suggest modifying the pedagogy by extrapolating up from the successful interventions used to teach learners who find maths challenging as opposed to diluting down methods that have had some measure of success with those pupils who find maths easy to learn. It's meant to be pragmatic.

'Teach the maths as it is to the learners as they are'.

Beliefs about maths are crucial: In a numeracy survey from 2014, 26% of adults believed that 'You cannot change your ability to do maths as some people are naturally good at maths, some are not'.

The curse of knowledge, defined as 'a cognitive bias that happens when an individual, communicating with other individuals, unknowingly assumes that they have the background knowledge to understand', scares me and ties in with Daniel Kahneman's observation that 'Even compelling causal statistics will not change long-held beliefs or beliefs rooted in personal experience'. This applies in maths and way beyond, too.

We often fail to look back far enough to check whether there is any bit of research or wisdom that might need re-visiting. Or maybe thinking 'Thank goodness we dropped that'.

'Nothing works for everyone'.

'Teach maths as it is to the learners as they are'.

Chapter 2

There is enough evidence out there to recognise that many learners have difficulty in remembering maths information. I also have a suspicion that sometimes, maybe too often, maths is taught on a 'remember this' principle (that is, rote learning).

This goes alongside another suspicion that some learners collude with this approach, having little interest in trying to understand maths.

Maths is a great subject for generalising and patterns and thus for using what you do know to work out what you don't know.

Chapter 3

Maths is very developmental. In this chapter, I set out a typical primary curriculum in a developmental way to show where topics come from and how they got there and thus highlight where gaps in learning and understanding are likely to create problems as the curriculum progresses.

This shows the structure of maths more clearly and thus how far back to go to start intervention. My experience is that it is usually much further back than we might at first think.

Whatever a learner learns when first experiencing a new topic becomes a dominant entry to the brain unless inhibited or unlearned. They need to get it right the first time.

Chapter 4

Failing to memorise and quickly retrieve the times tables facts is often pupils' first experience of persistent failure.

Rote learning can create disharmony and disappointment in families. If I could have a dollar for every parent or teacher who said to me, 'She learned the times tables last night, but she had forgotten them by the morning', I would be rich by now. Sharing an activity that results in persistent failure is not a bonding activity. I'm not convinced that saying it's 'the fun way to learn' helps. Or the 'quick' way. Or the 'easy' way. This just compounds the sense of failure.

A lesson should not begin with something that pupils can't do and maybe that they also hate.

Work with what they do know to take them to what they don't know. For example, the key facts for multiplication are 1, 2, 5, 10 and a knowledge of place value.

When a student has fallen behind in maths, it is very hard for them to catch up. One obvious reason they are behind is that they work more slowly than average.

Chapter 5

The most common answers to my (informal) survey of teachers from around the world as to the topics their students find most difficult are 'word problems, fractions, division and learning the basic facts'.

There's quite some difference between a strategy and a mnemonic. Do mnemonics hinder learning? Have they some use sometimes?

I am not a fan of such non-conceptual stuff as 'move the decimal point' as a way of dividing or multiplying by powers of 10. 'Look after your concepts and they'll look after you'.

Chapter 6

It will be ineffective to teach to the 'norm', whatever that is. So is it possible to teach to a wider range of learners? Can we teach in a way that minimises the number of learners who are disconnected from learning? And will the lessons we learn from the outliers help us to do that? I think the answer to both these questions is 'yes'.

In this chapter, I have focused on ten key factors that influence learning and on some of the interactions between these factors.

Can we extend Howard Gardner's theory of multiple intelligences to multiple memories? My experience is that not everyone has the same capacity of long-term memory for every topic; this is partly down to the brain and partly down to motivation and interests. It's one of the reasons why, in life, we get specialists. School is a bad place to be if you have weak long-term memories for spelling and for the basic facts and procedures in maths.

Making learners do maths at some arbitrary fast speed is very often counter-productive. This could include games like 'gunslinger' maths. Quick on the draw. Slowest die first.

Chapter 7

The hypothesis is that students have different cognitive styles. And teachers will too.

Kahneman sums up two styles: *System 1 operates automatically and quickly, with little or no effort and no sense of voluntary control. System 2 allocates attention to the effortful mental activities that demand it, including complex calculations.*

The lesson from metacognition for teachers is that *we* need to be flexible and adaptable in our thinking (and teaching) and encourage and develop this behaviour in our learners.

Chapter 8

Maths is a wonderful subject for using what you know to work out what you don't know. Facts link and concepts link.

'What else are you teaching?'

Do the overt linking and teaching of fractions, decimals and percentages together make an understanding of each of the three topics mutually supportive?

Chapter 9

I like Richard Skemp's warning that without an attached idea a symbol is empty and meaningless. This seems to me to be a strong caution about an over-reliance on rote learning and an argument for using appropriate visual images.

Beware of giving an incomplete story, maybe done to simplify things at the time (for example, the subtraction mantra, 'Take the little number from the big number'). And when multiplying by tens, 'Add some zeros'.

Look out for what's not there (a challenge!), such as the multiplication symbol in y = ab or in 'Six fives'.

And the classic, 'Find x'. 'Here it is!'

Chapter 10

Consistency brings security. Therefore, an idea, a fact needs to be correct as well as consistent.

I barely touch on time in this book but it is a topic with many inconsistencies.

Chapter 11

My argument is that visual images and materials are needed to secure an understanding of fractions.

At a basic level, the learner needs to make a (maybe counterintuitive) link of 'more' to 'smaller'. The *more* parts there are in a fraction, the *smaller* each part is. Inverse relationships can be challenging.

This is not a linear sequence: $\dfrac{1}{2}\ \dfrac{1}{3}\ \dfrac{1}{4}\ \dfrac{1}{5}\ \dfrac{1}{6}\ \dfrac{1}{7}\ \dfrac{1}{8}\ \dfrac{1}{9}$.

Yet we spring it on children. I think that visual images and the cutting up of fraction strips and squares are not an optional extra. They are essentials.

The question 'Is it bigger or smaller?' is apposite for work with fractions.

I worry about the idea of a fraction in its 'simplest form'. Many of my students found 'simplest' hard to come to terms with. An equivalent fraction is created when we multiply by 1, but related previous learning may have lodged in the brain, telling the learner that multiplying by 1 does not change the number. Equivalent fractions are about change but also about keeping the same value.

The Singapore bar model method for tackling word problems brings logical analysis into play and stops learners from rushing in without that all-important overview and analysis.

Chapter 12

Fractions are often the first maths topic that children meet that creates widespread anxiety and a sense of inconsistency.

Fractions challenge learners' sense of security in what they have learned for whole numbers.

If learners can place (correctly) fractions on a decimal number line, this is a strong indicator of understanding.

The $\times$ sign operates on both the top and the bottom numbers in fractions. For example,

$$\frac{4}{5} \times \frac{2}{3}$$

But the $+$ and $-$ signs operate only on the top numbers and then only if the bottom numbers of the fractions are the same. For example,

$$\frac{2}{7} + \frac{3}{7} = \frac{5}{7}$$

Word problems create great insecurity, mainly due to the number of variables that can be used to create such problems.

The Singapore model method provides a consistent and widely applicable approach to dealing with word problems.

Chapter 13

It is not only children with low maths ability who experience maths anxiety. More than three quarters of children with high maths anxiety are normal to high achievers on curriculum maths tests.

Anxiety is a complex issue: 'Over and above common cognitive demands and neurological representations and functions, performance in reading and arithmetic is influenced by a number of motivational and emotional factors such as: Need of achievement, task orientation, helplessness, depression, anxiety, self-esteem, self-concept, loneliness, locus of control, goal commitment, psychological adjustment, metacognition and self-regulation' (Lundberg, 2006).

In my (large sample) research, the top-rated anxiety item for all groups was 'Taking an end-of-term examination'.

One behaviour I had not explored when I set up that anxiety study was the 'no answer', the 'no attempt'. This is the behaviour where a student looks at a maths question, decides it's impossible or decides that they will get a wrong answer, and doesn't attempt it. There are several implications for teachers and test compilers here, not least the student who gives up at the first 'impossible' question he meets and doesn't skim through the rest of the test to find any 'possible' questions.

Expectations need to be comfortably challenging for learners or they will be demotivating.

Chapter 14

Assessment is sort of 'I want to know what you can and can't do' or, at the basic level, a number that sums up the level of achievement, whereas diagnosis is 'I want to know why you can or can't do it'.

In a diagnosis, I try to keep in mind the many, often interacting factors that are influencing what I am trying to measure.

A test needs to be useful and user-friendly. It should find out that useful information about learners, not just confirm their (the learners') opinion that they don't know anything about maths. The learner needs be positively and openly involved in the process. No input, no information.

Chapter 15

Communication is more effective when the person we are communicating with is open to receiving and engaging with the communication. We need to consider the affective domain in any communication. And the classroom ethos.

Giving out verbal instructions is a skill, and one factor in developing that skill is knowing how much to say in each chunk. And what to repeat.

Key Finding 1 from the National Research Council book *How People Learn* (2000): 'Students come to the classroom with preconceptions about how the world works. If their initial understanding is not engaged, they may fail to grasp the new concepts and information that they are taught, or they may learn them for the purposes of a test, but then revert to their preconceptions outside the classroom'.

Whatever current trend or ancient wisdom you follow to build a positive ethos in your classroom, your persona is the dominant factor.

What an 11-year-old is expected to know

Taken from a UK year 6 curriculum (for 11-year-olds). Selected highlights.

(I have not included algebra or geometry.)

Number: Number and place value

- Read, write, order and compare numbers up to 10,000,000 and determine the value of each digit. *(Note: It may be worth going up to a billion these days.)*
- Round any whole number to a required degree of accuracy.
- Solve number and practical problems that involve all of the above.

Number: Addition, subtraction, multiplication and division

- Multiply multi-digit numbers up to four digits by a two-digit whole number using the formal written method of long multiplication. *(Note: The method is specified in the curriculum document.)*
- Divide numbers up to four digits by a two-digit whole number using the formal written method of long division and interpret remainders as whole number remainders, fractions, or by rounding, as appropriate for the context.
- Divide numbers up to four digits by a two-digit number using the formal written method of short division where appropriate, interpreting remainders according to the context.
- Perform mental calculations, including with mixed operations and large numbers.
- Identify common factors, common multiples and prime numbers.
- Solve addition, subtraction, multiplication and division multi-step problems in contexts, deciding which operations and methods to use and why.
- Use estimation to check answers to calculations and determine, in the context of a problem, an appropriate degree of accuracy.

(Note: It also specifies that pupils continue to use all the multiplication tables to calculate.)

Number: Fractions (including decimals and percentages)

- Use common factors to simplify fractions and use common multiples to express fractions in the same denomination.
- Compare and order fractions, including fractions greater than 1.

- Add and subtract fractions with different denominators and mixed numbers, using the concept of equivalent fractions.
- Multiply simple pairs of proper fractions, writing the answer in its simplest form (for example, $\frac{1}{4} \times \frac{1}{2} = \frac{1}{8}$).
- Divide proper fractions by whole numbers (for example, $\frac{1}{3} \div 2 = \frac{1}{6}$).
- Associate a fraction with division and calculate decimal fraction equivalents (for example, 0.375) for a simple fraction (for example, $\frac{3}{8}$).
- Identify the value of each digit in numbers given to three decimal places and multiply and divide numbers by 10, 100 and 1,000 giving answers up to three decimal places.
- Multiply one-digit numbers with up to two decimal places by whole numbers.
- Use written division methods in cases where the answer has up to two decimal places.
- Solve problems that require answers to be rounded to specified degrees of accuracy.
- Recall and use equivalences between simple fractions, decimals and percentages, including in different contexts.

Ratio and proportion

- Solve problems involving the relative sizes of two quantities where missing values can be found by using integer multiplication and division facts.
- Solve problems involving the calculation of percentages (for example, of measures such as 15% of 360) and the use of percentages for comparison.
- Solve problems involving similar shapes where the scale factor is known or can be found.
- Solve problems involving unequal sharing and grouping using knowledge of fractions and multiples.

Measurement

- Solve problems involving the calculation and conversion of units of measure, using decimal notation up to three decimal places where appropriate.
- Use, read, write and convert between standard units, converting measurements of length, mass, volume and time from a smaller unit of measure to a larger unit, and vice versa, using decimal notation to up to three decimal places.
- Convert between miles and kilometres.
- Recognise that shapes with the same areas can have different perimeters and vice versa.
- Recognise when it is possible to use formulae for area and volume of shapes.
- Calculate, estimate and compare volumes of cubes and cuboids using standard units, including cubic centimetres (cm^3) and cubic metres (m^3), and extending to other units (for example, mm^3 and km^3).

Statistics

- Interpret and construct pie charts and line graphs and use these to solve problems.
- Calculate and interpret the mean as an average.

Appendix 2

Books and resources

Books, resources and papers from Steve Chinn

Books

'What to do when you can't tell the time'. 2009. SEN Books. *(This book does what it says in the title. There is a series of 'What to do when you can't …' books available from SEN Books.)*

The Routledge International Handbook of Dyscalculia and Mathematical Learning Difficulties. (edited by Steve Chinn). 2015. London: Routledge. *(This provides a comprehensive overview from authors around the world, covering classroom to neuroscience.)*

Mathematics for Dyslexics and Dyscalculics. 4th edn. (with Richard Ashcroft) 2017. Chichester: Wiley. *(This gives comprehensive coverage of theory and practice.)*

The Trouble with Maths: A Practical Guide to Helping Learners with Numeracy Difficulties. (4th edn due 2020) Abingdon: Routledge. *(This offers a pragmatic approach to teaching and learning maths. The first edition won a Nasen/TES book award in 2004.)*

More Trouble with Maths: A Complete Manual to Identifying and Diagnosing Mathematical Difficulties and Dyscalculia. (3rd edn). 2020. Abingdon: Routledge. *(This presents standardised tests and a range of other tests and clinical activities to use to create a comprehensive assessment/ diagnosis.)*

Resources

Steve Chinn's Dyscalculia Toolkit. *This is a collection of maths materials, including base-ten blocks, bead strings and Cuisenaire rods.* www.crossboweducation.com.

Numicon. Big Ideas (with Fiona Goddard and Liz Henning) 2017. Oxford: OUP.

Maths Learning Difficulties, Dyslexia and Dyscalculia. (2nd edn) London: JKP. *(This is a collection of lesson plans and supporting materials addressing the key ideas in maths for children who failed to grasp them securely the first timex.)*

Papers

(with Lane, C.) (1986) Learning by self-voice echo. *Academic Therapy.* 21. 477–481.

(with Bath, J.B. and Knox, D.E.) (1986) *The Test of Cognitive Style in Mathematics.* East Aurora, NY: Slosson.

Chinn, S.J. (1991) Factors to consider when designing a test protocol in mathematics for dyslexics. In Snowling, M and Thomson, M (eds) *Dyslexia: Integrating Theory and Practice.* London: Whurr 253–258.

Chinn, S.J. (1994) A study of the basic number fact skills of children from specialist dyslexic and 'mainstream' schools. *Dyslexia Review. 2,* 4–6.

Chinn S.J. (1995) A pilot study to compare aspects of arithmetic skill. *Dyslexia Review. 4*, 4–7.

Chinn, S.J. (1996) The relationship between the grades achieved in GCSE mathematics by 26 male students and their scores on the WISC. *Dyslexia Review. 7*, 8–9.

Chinn, S., McDonagh, D., van Elswijk, R., Harmsen, H., Kay, J., McPhillips, T., Power, A., and Skidmore, L. (2001) Classroom studies into cognitive style in mathematics for pupils with dyslexia in special education in the Netherlands, Ireland and the UK. *British Journal of Special Education. 28 (2)*, 80–85.

Chinn, S. (2008) Mathematics anxiety in secondary students in England. *Dyslexia. 15*, 61–68.

Chinn, S. (2010) The illusion of learning. *Dyslexia Review. 21*, 7–10.

Chinn, S. (2012) Beliefs, anxiety and avoiding failure in mathematics. *Child Development Research.* http://dx.doi.org/10.1155/2012/396071.

Chinn, S. (2013) Is the population really woefully bad at maths? *Mathematics Teaching (MT) 232*, 25–28.

Other books and reading

Ashlock, R.B. (2010) *Error Patterns in Computation*. 10th edn. New York: Allyn and Bacon.

Barton, C. (2018) *How I Wish I'd Taught Maths*. Woodbridge: John Catt.

Berch, D.B. (2005). Making sense of number sense: Implications for children with mathematical disabilities. *Journal of Learning Disabilities. 38 (4)* 333–339.

Berch, D.B. and Mazzocco, M.M.M. (eds) (2007) *Why is Math So Hard for Some Children?* Baltimore: Brookes Paul H.

Bransford, J.D., Brown, A. L. and Cocking R.R. (eds) (2000) *How People Learn*. Washington, DC: National Academy Press.

Burden, R. (2005) *Dyslexia and Self-concept*. Chichester: Wiley.

Buswell G.T. and Judd, C.M. (1925) *Summary of Educational Investigations Relating to Arithmetic*. Supplementary Educational Monographs. Chicago, IL: University of Chicago Press.

Butterworth, B. (2019) *Dyscalculia: From Science to Education*. Abingdon: Routledge.

Dowker, A. (2005) *Individual Differences in Arithmetic*. Hove: Psychology Press.

Geary, D.C. (1994) *Children's Mathematical Development. Research and Practical Applications*. Washington, DC: American Psychological Association.

Hattie, J. (2009) *Visible Learning*. London: Routledge.

Hodgen, J., Foster, C., Marks, R., & Brown, M. (2018). Evidence for Review of Mathematics Teaching: Improving Mathematics in Key Stages Two and Three: Evidence Review. London: Education Endowment Foundation. The report is available from: https://educationendowmentfoundation.org.uk/evidence-summaries/evidencereviews/improving-mathematics-in-key-stages-two-and-three/.

Hornigold, J. (2019) *Can I Tell you about Dyscalculia?*. London: Jessica Kingsley Publishers.

Kahneman, D. (2011) *Thinking, Fast and Slow*. London: Penguin.

Kho Tek Hong et al. (2009) *The Singapore Model Method*. Singapore: Ministry of Education.

Miles, T. and Miles, E. (eds) (2004) *Dyslexia and Mathematics*, 2nd edn. Abingdon: RoutledgeFalmer.

OFSTED (2008). Mathematics Report: 'Mathematics: Understanding the Score' (Report on Primary and Secondary Mathematics. www.childrens-mathematics.net/continuity_ofsted_maths.pdf.

Ramirez, G., Shaw, S.T. and Maloney, E.A. (2018) Maths anxiety: Past research, promising interventions and a new interpretation framework. *Educational Psychologist. 53*(3), 145–163, 10.1080/00461520.2018.1447384.

Rashid, S. and Brooks, G. (September 2010). The levels of attainment in literacy and numeracy of 13 to 19-year-olds in England, 1948–2009. *Literacy Today. 32*(1), 13–24.

Rosenshine, B. (2012) Principles of instruction research-based strategies that all teachers should know. *American Educator*. 12–39.

Seligman, M. (1998) *Learned Optimism*. New York: Pocket Books.

Skemp, R. R. (1986) *The Psychology of Learning Mathematics*. London: Penguin.

Usiskin, Z. (1998) Conceptions of school algebra and uses of variables, in Coxford, A. and Schulte, A. P. (eds) *Ideas of Algebra, K-12*, Reston, VA: NCTM.

Index

Page numbers in *italic* indicate figures. Page numbers in **bold** indicate tables.